M337 Unit B2
Mathematics: A Third Level Course

CW00337020

COMPLEX ANALYSIS

UNIT B2 CAUCHY'S THEOREM

Prepared by the Course Team

PLEX ANALYSIS COMPLEX ANALYSIS COMPL

Before working through this text, make sure that you have read the
Course Guide for M337 Complex Analysis.

The Open University, Walton Hall, Milton Keynes, MK7 6AA.

First published 1993. Reprinted 1995, 1998, 2002, 2006.

Copyright © 1993 The Open University

Edited, designed and typeset by the Open University using the Open University TEX
System.

Printed in Malta by Gutenberg Press Limited.

ISBN 0 7492 2180 1

This text forms part of an Open University Third Level Course. If you would like a copy
of *Studying with The Open University*, please write to the Central Enquiry Service,
PO Box 200, The Open University, Walton Hall, Milton Keynes, MK7 6YZ. If you have
not already enrolled on the Course and would like to buy this or other Open University
material, please write to Open University Educational Enterprises Ltd, 12 Cofferidge
Close, Stony Stratford, Milton Keynes, MK11 1BY, United Kingdom.

1.4

CONTENTS

INTRODUCTION

In this unit we present three of the most important results in complex analysis — *Cauchy's Theorem* and *Cauchy's Integral* and *Derivative Formulas*. These results lie at the very heart of complex analysis and give the subject much of its distinctive flavour.

In the previous unit we proved the following result, called the Closed Contour Theorem.

Closed Contour Theorem

Let the function f be continuous and have a primitive F on a region $\mathcal{R}$. Then

$$\int_{\Gamma} f(z)\,dz = 0,$$

for any closed contour Γ in $\mathcal{R}$.

Unit B1, Theorem 3.4

Cauchy's Theorem has the same conclusion as the Closed Contour Theorem. It states that if $\mathcal{R}$ is a region of a particular type and if f is analytic on $\mathcal{R}$, then

$$\int_{\Gamma} f(z)\,dz = 0,$$

for any closed contour Γ in $\mathcal{R}$. Cauchy's Theorem is discussed in Section 1, where we give an outline proof. The full details of this proof, which are rather involved, appear in Section 5.

The French mathematician Augustin-Louis Cauchy (1789–1857) developed the main theorems of complex analysis in a paper of 1826.

Section 2 is devoted to a discussion of Cauchy's remarkable Integral Formula, which expresses the value of an analytic function at any point *inside* a contour in terms of the values of the function *on* the contour. Using this Integral Formula, we prove a spectacular result, known as Liouville's Theorem, which states that any function which is entire (differentiable on $\mathbb{C}$) and bounded must be constant. This is a result which has no analogue in real analysis, where there are many non-constant functions, such as $x \longmapsto \sin x$ and $x \longmapsto e^{-x^2}$, which are differentiable on $\mathbb{R}$ and bounded.

In Section 3 we consider a further result due to Cauchy, which gives a formula (in terms of an integral) for the derivative of an analytic function. Once again there are many surprises: not only do we use integrals when we want to differentiate, but we find that if a function can be differentiated once on a region, then it can be differentiated as many times as we like — again, a result which has no analogue in real analysis.

After this wealth of unexpected results and new ideas, you may feel the need for a change of pace. This is provided by Section 4, a revision section, in which we consider examples of integrals that can be evaluated by a variety of methods.

Study guide

Most of the material in this unit is essential for your later work, and you should make sure that you become familiar with it. In particular, you will need to be familiar with the results of Sections 1, 2 and 3, and you should know how to use them. However, if you are short of time, then you can omit Section 5 on a first reading. The audio-tape section (Section 4) contains no new material, but reviews techniques from this unit and the previous one.

1 CAUCHY'S THEOREM

After working through this section, you should be able to:

(a) explain what is meant by a *simple-closed path* and a *simply-connected region*;

(b) state the Jordan Curve Theorem;

(c) state and use Cauchy's Theorem;

(d) state the Primitive Theorem and explain its role in the proof of Cauchy's Theorem;

(e) state and use the Contour Independence Theorem and the Shrinking Contour Theorem.

1.1 Simply-connected regions

In this subsection, we introduce the type of region we shall need in the statement of Cauchy's Theorem.

The Closed Contour Theorem (see the Introduction) tells us that if a function f is continuous on a region $\mathcal{R}$ and has a primitive on $\mathcal{R}$, then

$$\int_\Gamma f(z)\,dz = 0, \tag{$*$}$$

for any closed contour Γ in $\mathcal{R}$. It is tempting to conjecture that the same conclusion will hold if we assume that f is analytic on the region $\mathcal{R}$. Consider, however, the following example from *Unit B1*:

Unit B1, Example 2.2

$$\int_\Gamma \frac{1}{z}\,dz = 2\pi i,$$

where Γ is the unit circle $\{z : |z| = 1\}$. Here the integrand $f(z) = 1/z$ is analytic on the region $\mathcal{R} = \mathbb{C} - \{0\}$, which contains Γ (see Figure 1.1), and yet

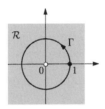

$$\int_\Gamma f(z)\,dz \neq 0.$$

Figure 1.1

In this example, however, the closed contour Γ encloses the point 0 and so the inside of Γ does not belong to the region $\mathcal{R}$. Cauchy realized that the key to proving $(*)$ for an analytic function f on a region $\mathcal{R}$ is to insist that the closed contour Γ *and* its inside lie in $\mathcal{R}$.

This idea leads us to make the following informal definition.

A region $\mathcal{R}$ is **simply-connected** if it has no holes in it.

For example, the regions in Figure 1.2 are simply-connected, as they have no holes in them.

  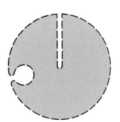

Figure 1.2

However the regions in Figure 1.3 are not simply-connected, as each has at least one hole in it.

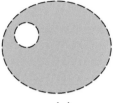 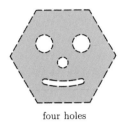

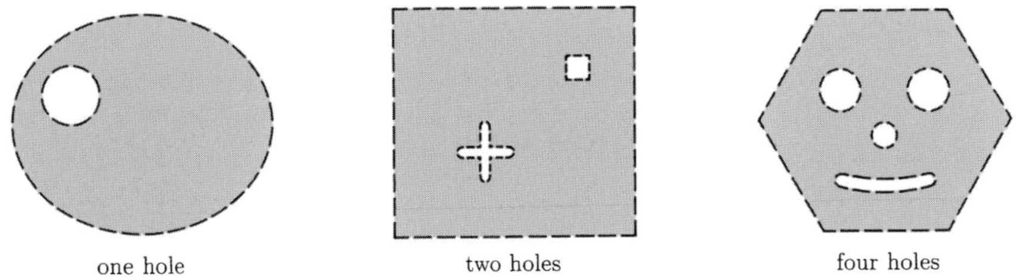

one hole   two holes   four holes

Figure 1.3

Problem 1.1

Which of the following regions are simply-connected?

(a)   (b)

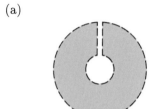   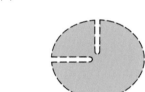

Figure 1.4   *Figure 1.5*

(c)   (d)

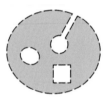   

Figure 1.6   *Figure 1.7*

(e) $\{z : -1 < \operatorname{Im} z < 1\}$ (f) $\{z : |z| > 3\}$ (g) $\mathbb{C}$

(h) $\{z : -\pi < \operatorname{Arg} z < \pi, 1 < |z| < 2\}$

In order to define a simply-connected region formally, we need the concept of a *simple-closed path*; this is a closed path which does not intersect itself. We also define the notion of a *simple path*.

Definition   A path $\Gamma : \gamma(t)$ $(t \in [a, b])$ is **simple-closed** if it is closed and γ is one-one on $[a, b[$.

A path $\Gamma : \gamma(t)$ $(t \in [a, b])$ is **simple** if γ is one-one on $[a, b]$.

Since a contour is a special case of a path, we also speak of **simple-closed contours** and **simple contours**.

Figure 1.8 illustrates these definitions.

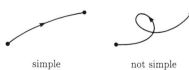

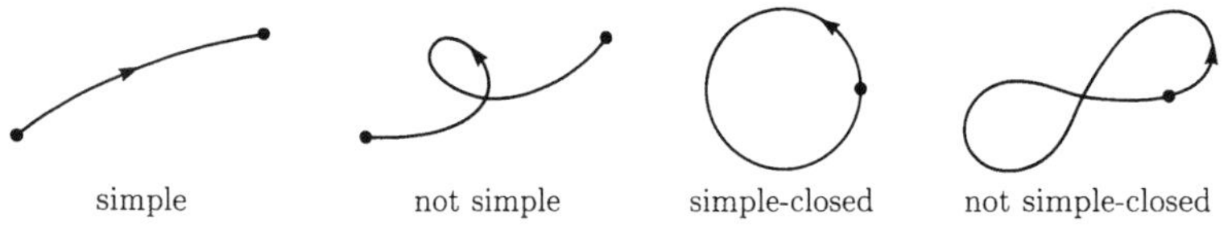

simple   not simple   simple-closed   not simple-closed

On the closed paths the dot denotes the point $\gamma(a) = \gamma(b)$.

Figure 1.8

A circle (which is a simple-closed path) has the property that it divides the complex plane into two regions — the inside of the circle and the outside of the circle. It seems clear that every simple-closed path must have an inside and an outside, but this is surprisingly difficult to prove (because some simple-closed paths can be very complicated). We therefore only state the general result, which is known as the Jordan Curve Theorem.

Theorem 1.1 Jordan Curve Theorem

If Γ is a simple-closed path, then the complement $\mathbb{C} - \Gamma$ of Γ is the union of two disjoint regions:

> a bounded region, called the **inside** of Γ, and
>
> an unbounded region, called the **outside** of Γ.

(See Figure 1.9.)

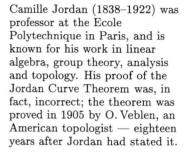

Camille Jordan (1838–1922) was professor at the Ecole Polytechnique in Paris, and is known for his work in linear algebra, group theory, analysis and topology. His proof of the Jordan Curve Theorem was, in fact, incorrect; the theorem was proved in 1905 by O. Veblen, an American topologist — eighteen years after Jordan had stated it.

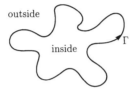

Figure 1.9
$\mathbb{C} - \Gamma = $ inside $\cup$ outside

The following problem will give you some idea of the difficulty of identifying the inside and outside of a complicated simple-closed path. For many simple-closed paths, however, it is clear which is the inside and which is the outside.

Problem 1.2

(a) Shade the inside of the following simple-closed path Γ. Which of the points A, B, C, D, E lie in the inside of Γ?

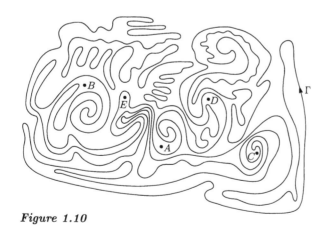

Figure 1.10

(b) Try to devise an algorithm for deciding whether a given point α lies in the inside of Γ. (Don't spend too long on this.)

We can now define a simply-connected region.

> **Definition**   A region $\mathcal{R}$ is **simply-connected** if, whenever Γ is a simple-closed path lying in $\mathcal{R}$, the inside of Γ also lies in $\mathcal{R}$.

For example, if $\mathcal{R}_1$ is the first region shown in Figure 1.11, and if Γ is *any* simple-closed path in $\mathcal{R}_1$ (such as the one shown), then the inside of Γ lies completely in $\mathcal{R}_1$; thus $\mathcal{R}_1$ is simply-connected. However, if $\mathcal{R}_2$ is the second region shown, and if Γ is the given path, then the inside of Γ does not lie in $\mathcal{R}_2$; thus $\mathcal{R}_2$ is not simply-connected.

$\mathcal{R}_1$ is simply-connected $\mathcal{R}_2$ is not simply-connected

Figure 1.11

There is one difficulty with the above definition of a simply-connected region. It is impossible to verify *directly* that a given region is simply-connected, since we would need to check that the inside of *every* simple-closed path lies in the region. Thus for *practical* purposes this formal definition is no better than our earlier informal one. We usually 'prove' that a given region $\mathcal{R}$ is simply-connected (when it is) by noting that $\mathcal{R}$ has no holes in it (as indicated in the solution to Problem 1.1).

It is possible, but quite tricky, to establish practical sufficient conditions for a region to be simply-connected. We shall not go into this.

1.2 Statement of Cauchy's Theorem

Now that we have defined simply-connected regions, we can state the central result of complex analysis — Cauchy's Theorem.

> ### Theorem 1.2 Cauchy's Theorem
>
> Let $\mathcal{R}$ be a simply-connected region, and let f be a function which is analytic on $\mathcal{R}$. Then
> $$\int_\Gamma f(z)\,dz = 0,$$
> for any closed contour Γ in $\mathcal{R}$.

For example, if we take $\mathcal{R}$ to be $\mathbb{C}$, Γ to be the unit circle $C = \{z : |z| = 1\}$, and $f(z) = z^2$, then the conditions of Cauchy's Theorem are satisfied. We deduce that
$$\int_C z^2\,dz = 0,$$
a result which also follows from the Closed Contour Theorem.

However, Cauchy's Theorem cannot be used to evaluate
$$\int_C z^{-1}\,dz,$$
since there is no simply-connected region $\mathcal{R}$ which contains C and on which the function $f(z) = z^{-1}$ is analytic.

Problem 1.3

Let $\mathcal{R}$ be the simply-connected region $\{z : |z| < 1\}$. Determine whether the conditions of Cauchy's Theorem are satisfied for each of the following functions f and contours Γ in $\mathcal{R}$.

(a) $f(z) = z^{-1}$ (b) $f(z) = e^z$ (c) $f(z) = \text{Log } z$

Figure 1.12

Figure 1.13

Figure 1.14

(d) $f(z) = (z - 3)^{-1}$ (e) $f(z) = z^2$ (f) $f(z) = |z|$

Figure 1.15

Figure 1.16

Figure 1.17

We now give an example to show how Cauchy's Theorem is applied in practice.

Example 1.1

Let Γ be the unit circle $\{z : |z| = 1\}$. Prove that

$$\int_\Gamma \frac{1}{z + 2}\, dz = 0.$$

Solution

We first choose a simply-connected region $\mathcal{R}$ containing Γ, on which the function $f(z) = 1/(z + 2)$ is analytic. An example of such a region is

$$\mathcal{R} = \left\{z : \text{Re } z > -\tfrac{3}{2}\right\},$$

since $\mathcal{R}$ does not contain the point -2 (see Figure 1.18). Then the conditions of Cauchy's Theorem are satisfied, and so

$$\int_\Gamma \frac{1}{z + 2}\, dz = 0. \quad \blacksquare$$

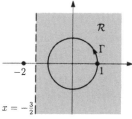

Figure 1.18

Problem 1.4

Prove that if Γ is any simple-closed contour and α is any point lying *outside* Γ, then

$$\int_\Gamma \frac{1}{z - \alpha}\, dz = 0.$$

We conclude this subsection with an outline of the proof of Cauchy's Theorem. Full details are given in Section 5.

Outline of a proof of Cauchy's Theorem

Let $\mathcal{R}$ be a simply-connected region, and let f be a function which is analytic on $\mathcal{R}$. We wish to prove that

$$\int_\Gamma f(z)\,dz = 0,$$

for any closed contour Γ in $\mathcal{R}$.

The proof is in three stages (the first two of which are special cases of Cauchy's Theorem). The aim is to show that the hypotheses of the Closed Contour Theorem (see the Introduction) are implied by those of Cauchy's Theorem, and so to establish the conclusion of Cauchy's Theorem by applying the Closed Contour Theorem.

(i) Cauchy's Theorem for a rectangular contour

We first prove Cauchy's Theorem when Γ is a rectangular contour in $\mathcal{R}$ (see Figure 1.19).

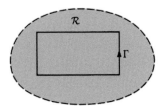

Figure 1.19

(ii) Cauchy's Theorem for a closed grid path

We then prove Cauchy's Theorem when Γ is a closed grid path in $\mathcal{R}$ (see Figure 1.20).

The definition of a grid path is given in *Unit B1*, Subsection 3.2.

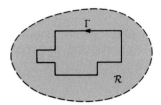

Figure 1.20

(iii) Primitive Theorem

Finally, we show that

> if a function f is analytic on a simply-connected region $\mathcal{R}$, then f has a primitive on $\mathcal{R}$.

This result is called the **Primitive Theorem** (or **Antiderivative Theorem**).

Cauchy's Theorem then follows from the Primitive Theorem and the Closed Contour Theorem.

1.3 Some consequences of Cauchy's Theorem

We now use Cauchy's Theorem to deduce some simple, but extremely useful, results. The first of these is a variant of the Contour Independence Theorem of *Unit B1*.

Theorem 1.3 Contour Independence Theorem

Let $\mathcal{R}$ be a simply-connected region, let f be a function which is analytic on $\mathcal{R}$, and let Γ_1 and Γ_2 be contours in $\mathcal{R}$ with the same initial point α and the same final point β. Then

$$\int_{\Gamma_1} f(z)\,dz = \int_{\Gamma_2} f(z)\,dz.$$

(See Figure 1.21.)

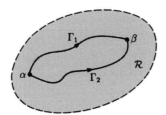

Figure 1.21

Problem 1.5

By applying Cauchy's Theorem to the closed contour $\Gamma_1 + \widetilde{\Gamma}_2$, prove Theorem 1.3.

Recall that $\widetilde{\Gamma}_2$ is the *reverse* of Γ_2.

Before stating our next result we need to establish a convention about integrals around simple-closed contours. Recall that a closed path $\Gamma : \gamma(t)$ $(t \in [a,b])$ is simple-closed if γ is one-one on $[a,b[$. This means that as t increases from a to b, the point $\gamma(t)$ traverses Γ exactly once, in either the clockwise or anticlockwise direction.

Convention

Unless otherwise specified, any simple-closed contour Γ appearing in a contour integral will be assumed to be traversed once anticlockwise, with the inside of Γ on the left. (Such a contour Γ may be described as *positively orientated*.)

Note that this convention accords with the standard parametrization of a circle.

The next result, which will be needed in Section 2 and elsewhere, shows that, under suitable conditions, we can replace an integral around a simple-closed contour by an integral around a circle.

Theorem 1.4 Shrinking Contour Theorem

Let $\mathcal{R}$ be a simply-connected region, let Γ be a simple-closed contour in $\mathcal{R}$, let α be a point inside Γ, and let g be a function which is analytic on $\mathcal{R} - \{\alpha\}$. Then

$$\int_\Gamma g(z)\,dz = \int_C g(z)\,dz,$$

where C is any circle with centre α, lying inside Γ (see Figure 1.22).

The reason for choosing C to be a *circle* will emerge in Section 2.

Proof

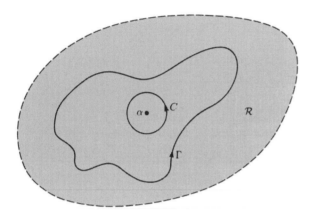

Figure 1.22

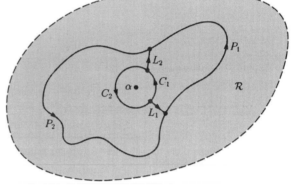

Figure 1.23

Draw two simple contours L_1 and L_2, which do not intersect each other, from the circle C to the contour Γ, thereby dividing Γ into two parts P_1 and P_2, and C into two parts C_1 and C_2, as shown in Figure 1.23. Let $\mathcal{R}_1$ be a simply-connected region contained in $\mathcal{R}$, and containing the contour $\Gamma_1 = L_1 + P_1 + \widetilde{L}_2 + \widetilde{C}_1$, but not the point α (see Figure 1.24). Similarly, let $\mathcal{R}_2$ be a simply-connected region contained in $\mathcal{R}$, and containing the contour $\Gamma_2 = L_2 + P_2 + \widetilde{L}_1 + \widetilde{C}_2$, but not the point α (see Figure 1.25).

We need $\mathcal{R}$ to be simply-connected, so that $\mathcal{R}_1$ and $\mathcal{R}_2$ will also be simply-connected and Cauchy's Theorem can be applied.

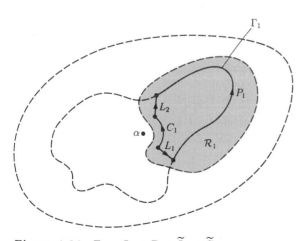

Figure 1.24 $\Gamma_1 = L_1 + P_1 + \widetilde{L}_2 + \widetilde{C}_1$

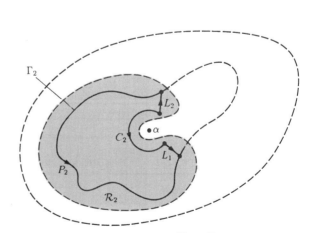

Figure 1.25 $\Gamma_2 = L_2 + P_2 + \widetilde{L}_1 + \widetilde{C}_2$

Applying Cauchy's Theorem to the function g around the contour Γ_1 in the region $\mathcal{R}_1$, we obtain

$$\int_{L_1} g(z)\,dz + \int_{P_1} g(z)\,dz + \int_{\widetilde{L}_2} g(z)\,dz + \int_{\widetilde{C}_1} g(z)\,dz = 0.$$

Similarly, applying Cauchy's Theorem to the function g around the contour Γ_2 in the region $\mathcal{R}_2$, we obtain

$$\int_{L_2} g(z)\,dz + \int_{P_2} g(z)\,dz + \int_{\widetilde{L}_1} g(z)\,dz + \int_{\widetilde{C}_2} g(z)\,dz = 0.$$

If we add these two equations, the integrals along L_1 and $\widetilde{L}_1$ cancel, as do the integrals along L_2 and $\widetilde{L}_2$, leaving

$$\int_{P_1} g(z)\,dz + \int_{P_2} g(z)\,dz + \int_{\widetilde{C}_1} g(z)\,dz + \int_{\widetilde{C}_2} g(z)\,dz = 0;$$

that is,

$$\int_{P_1} g(z)\,dz + \int_{P_2} g(z)\,dz = \int_{C_1} g(z)\,dz + \int_{C_2} g(z)\,dz.$$

Thus

$$\int_{\Gamma} g(z)\,dz = \int_{C} g(z)\,dz. \quad \blacksquare$$

For example,

$$\int_{\widetilde{L}_1} g(z)\,dz = -\int_{L_1} g(z)\,dz$$

by the Reverse Contour Theorem (*Unit B1*, Theorem 2.3).

Remark The technique used here of introducing extra contours, in order to obtain suitable closed contours to which Cauchy's Theorem can be applied, is a standard technique in complex analysis.

Problem 1.6

Use the Shrinking Contour Theorem to evaluate the integral

$$\int_{\Gamma} z^{-1}\,dz,$$

where Γ is the ellipse $\{z = x + iy : \dfrac{x^2}{9} + \dfrac{y^2}{4} = 1\}$.

2 THE INTEGRAL FORMULA

After working through this section, you should be able to:

(a) state and use Cauchy's Integral Formula, in particular to evaluate integrals;

(b) state and use Liouville's Theorem.

2.1 Cauchy's Integral Formula

In this section we present a remarkable result which expresses the values of an analytic function f *inside* a simple-closed contour Γ in terms of the values of f *on* Γ. The formula involves an integral, and it can also be used in reverse to evaluate integrals, as you will see. Its proof will be given in Subsection 2.2.

Theorem 2.1 Cauchy's Integral Formula

Let $\mathcal{R}$ be a simply-connected region, let Γ be a simple-closed contour in $\mathcal{R}$, and let f be a function which is analytic on $\mathcal{R}$. Then

$$f(\alpha) = \frac{1}{2\pi i} \int_{\Gamma} \frac{f(z)}{z - \alpha}\,dz,$$

for any point α inside Γ. (See Figure 2.1.)

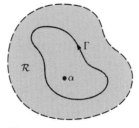

Figure 2.1

Cauchy's Integral Formula has great theoretical importance, in that the representation of $f(\alpha)$ in terms of an integral can be used to find properties of the function f. For example, we shall be using it to derive a formula for the derivative f' in Section 3, and to prove Taylor's Theorem in the next unit.

More important for our present purposes are the practical consequences of Cauchy's Integral Formula. In one direction, it tells us that we can find the value of $f(\alpha)$ by integrating the function

$$z \longmapsto f(z)/(z - \alpha)$$

around the contour Γ. Often, however, it is more useful to reverse the procedure and use the Integral Formula in the form

$$\int_\Gamma \frac{f(z)}{z - \alpha}\, dz = 2\pi i\, f(\alpha)$$

to evaluate an integral of this type in terms of the value of $f(\alpha)$. The following examples should make the method clear.

Recall our convention from Section 1 that Γ is assumed to be traversed once anticlockwise.

Example 2.1

Evaluate $\displaystyle\int_\Gamma \frac{e^z}{z - 1}\, dz$, where Γ is the circle $\{z : |z| = 2\}$.

Solution

We use Cauchy's Integral Formula with $f(z) = e^z$, $\alpha = 1$ and $\mathcal{R} = \mathbb{C}$. Then $\mathcal{R}$ is simply-connected, Γ is a simple-closed contour in $\mathcal{R}$, and α lies inside Γ (see Figure 2.2). Also, f is analytic on $\mathcal{R}$.

Always remember to check that the conditions apply, before you use this (or any other) formula.

It follows from the Integral Formula that

$$\int_\Gamma \frac{e^z}{z - 1}\, dz = 2\pi i\, f(1)$$

$$= 2\pi i e^1 = 2\pi e i. \quad\blacksquare$$

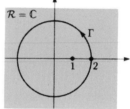

Figure 2.2

Problem 2.1

Use Cauchy's Integral Formula to evaluate each of the following integrals.

(a) $\displaystyle\int_\Gamma \frac{\sin z}{z + i}\, dz$, where Γ is the circle $\{z : |z| = 2\}$.

(b) $\displaystyle\int_\Gamma \frac{3z}{z + 1}\, dz$, where Γ is the circle $\{z : |z - 3| = 5\}$.

When the integrand is not as simple as those considered above, we need to be careful in choosing the function f, as the following example illustrates.

Example 2.2

Evaluate $\displaystyle\int_\Gamma \frac{z^2 + 3}{z(z - 2)}\, dz$, where Γ is the circle $\{z : |z| = 1\}$.

Solution

Looking at the denominator, we see that 0 and 2 are the only points where the integrand is not defined. Of these two points, only 0 lies inside Γ. We therefore take $f(z) = (z^2 + 3)/(z - 2)$ and $\alpha = 0$, and let $\mathcal{R}$ be any simply-connected region which contains Γ but not the point 2; for example, $\mathcal{R} = \{z : \operatorname{Re} z < \tfrac{3}{2}\}$. Then Γ is a simple-closed contour in $\mathcal{R}$, and α lies inside Γ (see Figure 2.3). Also, f is analytic on $\mathcal{R}$.

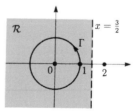

Figure 2.3

It follows from Cauchy's Integral Formula that

$$\int_\Gamma \frac{z^2 + 3}{z(z-2)}\, dz = \int_\Gamma \frac{(z^2+3)/(z-2)}{z}\, dz$$

$$= \int_\Gamma \frac{f(z)}{z-0}\, dz$$

$$= 2\pi i\, f(0)$$

$$= 2\pi i \left(-\tfrac{3}{2}\right) = -3\pi i. \quad \blacksquare$$

Problem 2.2

Use Cauchy's Integral Formula to evaluate each of the following integrals.

(a) $\displaystyle\int_\Gamma \frac{e^{3z}}{z^2 - 4}\, dz$, where $\Gamma = \{z : |z - 1| = 2\}$.

(b) $\displaystyle\int_\Gamma \frac{\cos 2z}{z(z^2 + 4)}\, dz$, where Γ is the square contour with vertices

$$1 + i, -1 + i, -1 - i, 1 - i.$$

As we have seen, Cauchy's Integral Formula can be used to evaluate integrals of the form

$$\int_\Gamma \frac{f(z)}{z - \alpha}\, dz.$$

By using partial fractions, we can extend the range of applicability of Cauchy's Integral Formula to integrals like

$$\int_\Gamma \frac{e^{2z}}{z^2 + 1}\, dz,$$

in which the denominator is a polynomial with distinct linear factors. In this case, since $z^2 + 1 = (z - i)(z + i)$, the partial fraction expansion has the form

$$\frac{1}{z^2 + 1} = \frac{1}{(z-i)(z+i)} = \frac{A}{z+i} + \frac{B}{z-i},$$

There is one term for each factor.

where A and B are complex numbers. One way of determining A and B is as follows.

Multiplying both sides by $z^2 + 1$, we obtain

$$1 = A(z - i) + B(z + i).$$

Comparing the coefficients of z and constants, we obtain

$$z: \quad 0 = A + B$$
$$1: \quad 1 = -Ai + Bi.$$

Alternatively, putting $z = i$ in this equation gives

$$1 = 2Bi,$$

so that $B = -i/2$. Similarly, putting $z = -i$ gives

$$A = i/2.$$

Solving these simultaneous equations gives $A = i/2$, $B = -i/2$. Thus

$$\frac{1}{z^2 + 1} = \frac{i/2}{z+i} - \frac{i/2}{z-i}. \qquad (*)$$

The results of the following problem will be useful in Problem 2.4 and Example 2.4.

Problem 2.3

Write each of the following expressions in partial fractions.

(a) $\dfrac{1}{z^2 - z}$ (b) $\dfrac{1}{z(z-2)}$

We now show how partial fractions can be used in conjunction with Cauchy's Integral Formula.

Example 2.3

Evaluate $\int_\Gamma \dfrac{e^{2z}}{z^2+1}\,dz$, where Γ is the circle $\{z : |z-1| = 2\}$.

Solution

Using the partial fractions $(*)$ obtained above, we have

$$\int_\Gamma \frac{e^{2z}}{z^2+1}\,dz = \frac{i}{2}\int_\Gamma \frac{e^{2z}}{z+i}\,dz - \frac{i}{2}\int_\Gamma \frac{e^{2z}}{z-i}\,dz.$$

We now use Cauchy's Integral Formula with $f(z) = e^{2z}$, $\mathcal{R} = \mathbb{C}$, and $\alpha = -i$ and i (in turn). Then $\mathcal{R}$ is simply-connected, Γ is a simple-closed contour in $\mathcal{R}$, $-i$ and i lie inside Γ and f is analytic on $\mathcal{R}$ (see Figure 2.4). Thus

$$\int_\Gamma \frac{e^{2z}}{z+i}\,dz = 2\pi i f(-i) = 2\pi i e^{-2i}$$

and

$$\int_\Gamma \frac{e^{2z}}{z-i}\,dz = 2\pi i f(i) = 2\pi i e^{2i}.$$

Putting all this together, we obtain

$$\begin{aligned}
\int_\Gamma \frac{e^{2z}}{z^2+1}\,dz &= \frac{i}{2}(2\pi i e^{-2i}) - \frac{i}{2}(2\pi i e^{2i})\\
&= \pi(e^{2i} - e^{-2i})\\
&= 2\pi i \sin 2. \quad\blacksquare
\end{aligned}$$

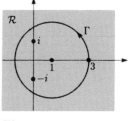

Figure 2.4

Recall that
$$\sin z = (e^{iz} - e^{-iz})/(2i).$$

Problem 2.4

Use Cauchy's Integral Formula to evaluate

$$\int_\Gamma \frac{\cos 3z}{z^2 - z}\,dz, \text{ where } \Gamma \text{ is the circle } \{z : |z-1| = 2\}.$$

The following example illustrates how we can sometimes save some effort when partial fractions are involved.

Example 2.4

Evaluate $\int_\Gamma \dfrac{\cos z}{z(z^2-4)}\,dz$, where Γ is the circle $\{z : |z-2| = 3\}$.

Solution

It is tempting to expand $1/(z(z^2 - 4))$ in partial fractions and proceed as in Example 2.3. However, an alternative approach involving a simpler partial fraction expansion is as follows.

First note that

$$z(z^2 - 4) = z(z-2)(z+2),$$

and that 0 and 2 lie inside Γ but -2 lies outside Γ. Also, using partial fractions, we have

$$\frac{1}{z(z-2)} = -\frac{1}{2}\cdot\frac{1}{z} + \frac{1}{2}\cdot\frac{1}{z-2},$$

and so

$$\int_\Gamma \frac{\cos z}{z(z^2-4)}\,dz = -\frac{1}{2}\int_\Gamma \frac{(\cos z)/(z+2)}{z}\,dz + \frac{1}{2}\int_\Gamma \frac{(\cos z)/(z+2)}{z-2}\,dz.$$

This suggests combining $(z+2)$ with $\cos z$ to form $f(z)$.

See Problem 2.3(b).

We now let $\mathcal{R}$ be any simply-connected region containing Γ but not the point -2; for example, $\mathcal{R} = \{z : \operatorname{Re} z > -\frac{3}{2}\}$ (see Figure 2.5). Applying Cauchy's Integral Formula with $f(z) = (\cos z)/(z+2)$, which is analytic on $\mathcal{R}$, and $\alpha = 0$ and 2 (in turn), gives

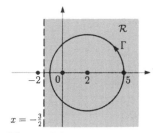

$$\int_{\Gamma} \frac{(\cos z)/(z+2)}{z}\, dz = 2\pi i\, f(0)$$
$$= 2\pi i \cdot \tfrac{1}{2} = \pi i,$$

and

$$\int_{\Gamma} \frac{(\cos z)/(z+2)}{z-2}\, dz = 2\pi i\, f(2)$$
$$= 2\pi i \cdot \frac{\cos 2}{4} = \tfrac{1}{2}\pi i \cos 2.$$

Figure 2.5

Putting all this together, we obtain

$$\int_{\Gamma} \frac{\cos z}{z(z^2 - 4)}\, dz = -\tfrac{1}{2} \cdot \pi i + \tfrac{1}{2} \cdot \left(\tfrac{1}{2}\pi i \cos 2\right)$$
$$= \tfrac{1}{4}\pi i (-2 + \cos 2). \quad \blacksquare$$

Problem 2.5

(a) Use the partial fraction expansion

$$\frac{1}{z^4 - 1} = \frac{1}{4}\left(\frac{1}{z-1} - \frac{1}{z+1} + \frac{i}{z-i} - \frac{i}{z+i}\right),$$

to evaluate

$$\int_{\Gamma} \frac{e^z}{z^4 - 1}\, dz,$$

when Γ is

(i) the ellipse $\{z = x + iy : 4x^2 + 9y^2 = 36\}$;

(ii) the rectangular contour with vertices $\frac{1}{2} + 2i$, $-\frac{1}{2} + 2i$, $-\frac{1}{2} - 2i$, $\frac{1}{2} - 2i$.

(b) Confirm your answer to part (a)(ii) by using the approach of Example 2.4.

Using the approaches just described, we can evaluate *any* integral of the form

$$\int_{\Gamma} \frac{g(z)}{p(z)}\, dz,$$

where Γ is a simple-closed contour, g is a function which is analytic on some simply-connected region $\mathcal{R}$ containing Γ, and $p(z)$ is a polynomial with *distinct* roots (none of which lies on Γ). But we cannot yet evaluate integrals involving polynomials with repeated roots in the denominator, such as

$$\int_{\Gamma} \frac{e^z}{(z-1)^2}\, dz.$$

Methods for dealing with such integrals will be discussed in Section 3. (A general strategy is given in Section 4.)

This is because any such polynomial $p(z)$ can be expressed as a product of n distinct linear factors (by the Fundamental Theorem of Algebra, discussed at the end of this section).

2.2 The proof of Cauchy's Integral Formula

We now present a proof of Cauchy's Integral Formula.

Theorem 2.1 Cauchy's Integral Formula

Let $\mathcal{R}$ be a simply-connected region, let Γ be a simple-closed contour in $\mathcal{R}$, and let f be a function which is analytic on $\mathcal{R}$. Then

$$f(\alpha) = \frac{1}{2\pi i} \int_\Gamma \frac{f(z)}{z - \alpha}\, dz,$$

for any point α inside Γ.

Before we give the proof, we make two introductory remarks.

Remarks

1 A standard method for proving that a complex number I is zero is to show that, for some positive constant K,

$$|I| \le K\varepsilon, \qquad \text{for each positive number } \varepsilon. \tag{2.1}$$

To see why this proves that $I = 0$, suppose that $I \ne 0$, and take $\varepsilon = \frac{1}{2}|I|/K$ in Inequality (2.1). Then

$$0 < |I| \le \tfrac{1}{2}|I|,$$

which is false. Thus $I = 0$.

2 During the proof, we shall need the fact that

$$\int_C \frac{1}{z - \alpha}\, dz = 2\pi i,$$

where C is any circle with centre α.

In *Unit B1*, Example 2.2, we proved this result in the case $\alpha = 0$, $r = 1$.

To prove this, we use the standard parametrization

$$\gamma(t) = \alpha + re^{it} \qquad (t \in [0, 2\pi]),$$

where r is the radius of the circle. Then $\gamma'(t) = rie^{it}$, and we have

$$\int_C \frac{1}{z - \alpha}\, dz = \int_0^{2\pi} \frac{rie^{it}}{re^{it}}\, dt$$

$$= \int_0^{2\pi} i\, dt = 2\pi i.$$

We now prove the Integral Formula. The basic tools are the Shrinking Contour Theorem (Theorem 1.4) and the Estimation Theorem (*Unit B1*, Theorem 4.1).

Proof of Cauchy's Integral Formula

There are four steps in the proof.

(a) Consider the integral

$$\int_\Gamma \frac{f(z)}{z - \alpha}\, dz.$$

By the Shrinking Contour Theorem, we can replace Γ by any circle C with centre α, lying inside Γ, to obtain

$$\int_\Gamma \frac{f(z)}{z - \alpha}\, dz = \int_C \frac{f(z)}{z - \alpha}\, dz.$$

The radius r of C will be chosen in Step (c).

Here we apply the Shrinking Contour Theorem with
$$g(z) = f(z)/(z - \alpha).$$
Such a circle C exists, since the inside of Γ is an open set.

(b) Let

$$I = \int_C \frac{f(z)}{z - \alpha}\, dz - 2\pi i\, f(\alpha).$$

To prove the theorem, we need to show that the complex number I is equal to zero.

By Remark 2, we can replace the $2\pi i$ by

$$\int_C \frac{1}{z-\alpha}\,dz,$$

giving

$$
\begin{aligned}
I &= \int_C \frac{f(z)}{z-\alpha}\,dz - f(\alpha)\int_C \frac{1}{z-\alpha}\,dz \\
&= \int_C \left(\frac{f(z)}{z-\alpha} - \frac{f(\alpha)}{z-\alpha}\right)dz \\
&= \int_C \frac{f(z)-f(\alpha)}{z-\alpha}\,dz.
\end{aligned}
$$

We can take $f(\alpha)$ inside the integral, because it is a constant.

(c) We now use the Estimation Theorem to give an upper estimate for $|I|$. The length of C is easy to find: it is just $2\pi r$, the circumference of the circle. To find an upper estimate for

$$\left|\frac{f(z)-f(\alpha)}{z-\alpha}\right|$$

on C, we use the fact that f is continuous at α. Thus

for each $\varepsilon > 0$, there is $\delta > 0$ such that

$$|z-\alpha| < \delta \quad\Longrightarrow\quad |f(z)-f(\alpha)| < \varepsilon.$$

If we now choose the radius r to be any positive number less than δ, then we can write

$$
\begin{aligned}
\left|\frac{f(z)-f(\alpha)}{z-\alpha}\right| &= \frac{|f(z)-f(\alpha)|}{|z-\alpha|} \\
&< \frac{\varepsilon}{r}, \qquad \text{for } z \in C.
\end{aligned}
$$

This theorem states that

$$\left|\int_\Gamma f(z)\,dz\right| \le ML,$$

where M is an upper estimate of $|f(z)|$ on Γ, and L is the length of Γ.

Recall that
$\quad f$ differentiable at α
$\quad\Longrightarrow$
$\quad f$ continuous at α
(Theorem 1.1, *Unit A4*).

Note that $|z-\alpha| = r$, for $z \in C$.

It follows from the Estimation Theorem, with $M = \varepsilon/r$ and $L = 2\pi r$, that

$$|I| \le \frac{\varepsilon}{r}\cdot 2\pi r = 2\pi\varepsilon.$$

(d) Finally, we use the result of Remark 1. Since $|I| \le 2\pi\varepsilon$, for each positive number ε, we obtain $I = 0$. This concludes the proof. ∎

Problem 2.6

At which points in the above proof did we use the fact that f is analytic on $\mathcal{R}$?

Problem 2.7

Let $\mathcal{R}$ be a simply-connected region, let $C = \{z : |z-\alpha| = r\}$ be a circle contained in $\mathcal{R}$, and let f be a function which is analytic on $\mathcal{R}$. Prove that

$$f(\alpha) = \frac{1}{2\pi}\int_0^{2\pi} f(\alpha + re^{it})\,dt.$$

(This result is called **Gauss' Mean Value Theorem**: it tells us that the value of f at the centre of C is the 'average' of the values of f on C.)

2.3 Liouville's Theorem

We come now to one of the most surprising results in complex analysis. In your study of real functions, you will have met many functions which are differentiable at all values of x, and which are bounded; examples of such functions are $f(x) = \sin x$, $f(x) = \exp(-x^2)$, and $f(x) = \tan^{-1} x$ (see Figure 2.6).

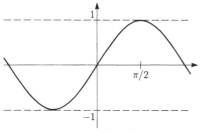

$f(x) = \sin x,\ |\sin x| \le 1$

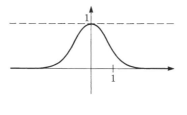

$f(x) = \exp(-x^2),\ |\exp(-x^2)| \le 1$

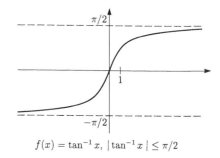

$f(x) = \tan^{-1} x,\ |\tan^{-1} x| \le \pi/2$

Figure 2.6

In complex analysis, however, the class of all bounded functions which are entire (that is, differentiable at all values of z) is very restricted — it consists only of the constant functions!

Theorem 2.2 Liouville's Theorem

If f is a bounded entire function, then f is constant.

Joseph Liouville (1809–1882) proved this result in the early 1840s. The first *published* proof was given by Cauchy in 1851.

Another way of expressing this result is to say that

> if f is a non-constant entire function, then f must be unbounded.

Before proving Liouville's Theorem, we give two problems which test your understanding of its statement.

Problem 2.8 _____

What is wrong with the following reasoning?
Since $f(z) = \sin z$ is entire and $|\sin z| \le 1$, for all $z \in \mathbb{C}$, the sine function is constant, by Liouville's Theorem.

Problem 2.9 _____

Use Liouville's Theorem to prove that the function $f(z) = \exp(i|z|)$ is not an entire function.

We come now to the proof of Liouville's Theorem. In order to prove that f is a constant function, we choose an arbitrary point α and show that $f(\alpha) = f(0)$. To do this, we use Cauchy's Integral Formula to write

$$f(\alpha) = \frac{1}{2\pi i} \int_C \frac{f(z)}{z - \alpha}\, dz,$$

where C is a circle with centre 0 surrounding α.

If the radius of C is very large, then the points α and 0 (as seen from C) will look very close. We use this fact to show that $f(\alpha) - f(0) = 0$.

Proof of Liouville's Theorem

This proof may be omitted on a first reading.

The proof is in four steps.

(a) Let α be any point of $\mathbb{C}$, and let C be a circle with centre 0 and radius r, where $r > |\alpha|$ (see Figure 2.7). Since f is analytic on $\mathbb{C}$, and $\mathbb{C}$ is simply-connected, we can apply Cauchy's Integral Formula to give

$$f(\alpha) = \frac{1}{2\pi i} \int_C \frac{f(z)}{z - \alpha}\, dz \quad \text{and} \quad f(0) = \frac{1}{2\pi i} \int_C \frac{f(z)}{z}\, dz.$$

Thus

$$f(\alpha) - f(0) = \frac{1}{2\pi i} \int_C \left(\frac{1}{z - \alpha} - \frac{1}{z} \right) f(z)\, dz$$

$$= \frac{\alpha}{2\pi i} \int_C \frac{f(z)}{z(z - \alpha)}\, dz.$$

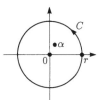

Figure 2.7

(b) We now estimate this integral.

Since, by assumption, f is bounded, there exists a number K such that

$$|f(z)| \le K, \qquad \text{for all } z \in \mathbb{C}.$$

Also, for each z on C, we have $|z| = r$ and so, by the backwards form of the Triangle Inequality,

$$|z - \alpha| \ge |z| - |\alpha| = r - |\alpha|, \qquad \text{for } z \in C.$$

It follows that

$$\left| \frac{f(z)}{z(z - \alpha)} \right| \le \frac{K}{r(r - |\alpha|)}, \qquad \text{for } z \in C.$$

Using the Estimation Theorem, with $M = K/(r(r - |\alpha|))$ and $L = 2\pi r$, we obtain

$$|f(\alpha) - f(0)| = \left| \frac{\alpha}{2\pi i} \int_C \frac{f(z)}{z(z - \alpha)}\, dz \right|$$

$$\le \frac{|\alpha|}{2\pi} \cdot \frac{K}{r(r - |\alpha|)} \cdot 2\pi r$$

$$= \frac{K|\alpha|}{r - |\alpha|}.$$

(c) We next show that, for each positive number ε, we can choose r so large that $|f(\alpha) - f(0)| < \varepsilon$. Now

$$\frac{K|\alpha|}{r - |\alpha|} < \varepsilon \quad \Longleftrightarrow \quad r - |\alpha| > |\alpha|(K/\varepsilon)$$

$$\Longleftrightarrow \quad r > |\alpha|(1 + K/\varepsilon).$$

It follows that

$$\text{if } r > |\alpha|(1 + K/\varepsilon), \text{ then } |f(\alpha) - f(0)| < \varepsilon.$$

(d) It now follows from Remark 1 (in Subsection 2.2) that

$$f(\alpha) - f(0) = 0.$$

Since this is true for any point $\alpha \in \mathbb{C}$, we deduce that

$$f(\alpha) = f(0), \qquad \text{for all } \alpha \in \mathbb{C};$$

that is, f is a constant function. ∎

Remark Liouville's Theorem can be used to prove the **Fundamental Theorem of Algebra**. This states that

if

$$p(z) = a_0 + a_1 z + \cdots + a_n z^n \qquad (z \in \mathbb{C}),$$

where $n \ge 1$ and $a_0, a_1, \ldots, a_n \in \mathbb{C}$, with $a_n \ne 0$,

then the function p has at least one zero.

The idea of the proof is to suppose that $p(z) \ne 0$, for all $z \in \mathbb{C}$, and then obtain a contradiction (as we now outline).

Note that the function
$$1/p(z) \qquad (z \in \mathbb{C})$$
is entire (since $p \neq 0$ on $\mathbb{C}$). It is also bounded on $\mathbb{C}$, since

$$\left| \frac{1}{p(z)} \right| = \frac{1}{|z|^n |a_n + a_{n-1}/z + \cdots + a_0/z^n|} \to 0 \text{ as } z \to \infty.$$

It is here that more detail is needed in the proof. In particular, we have not yet defined the limit as $z \to \infty$.

Hence $1/p$ is constant, by Liouville's Theorem, and so p is constant. This is a contradiction, since $n \geq 1$, and so p must have at least one zero.

It follows that $p(z)$ can be expressed as the product of n linear factors
$$p(z) = a_n(z - \alpha_1)(z - \alpha_2) \ldots (z - \alpha_n),$$
where some or all of the zeros $\alpha_1, \alpha_2, \ldots, \alpha_n$ may be repeated.

If α_1 is a zero of p, then divide $p(z)$ by $(z - \alpha_1)$ and repeat the process.

Later in the course we give an alternative proof of the Fundamental Theorem of Algebra.

3 THE DERIVATIVE FORMULAS

After working through this section, you should be able to:

(a) state and use Cauchy's nth Derivative Formula, in particular to evaluate integrals;

(b) state and use the Analyticity of Derivatives Theorem.

3.1 Cauchy's First Derivative Formula

In the previous section you saw that if f is an analytic function on a simply-connected region $\mathcal{R}$, and if Γ is a simple-closed contour in $\mathcal{R}$, then

$$f(\alpha) = \frac{1}{2\pi i} \int_\Gamma \frac{f(z)}{z - \alpha} \, dz, \qquad (3.1)$$

This is Cauchy's Integral Formula.

for each point α inside Γ. We now show that there is a similar formula for the first derivative f', namely

$$f'(\alpha) = \frac{1}{2\pi i} \int_\Gamma \frac{f(z)}{(z - \alpha)^2} \, dz.$$

Note that this is the result you would get if you threw rigour to the winds, and differentiated the right-hand side of Equation (3.1) with respect to α:

$$\frac{d}{d\alpha} \left(\frac{1}{2\pi i} \int_\Gamma \frac{f(z)}{z - \alpha} \, dz \right) = \frac{1}{2\pi i} \int_\Gamma \frac{d}{d\alpha} \left(\frac{1}{z - \alpha} \right) f(z) \, dz$$

$$= \frac{1}{2\pi i} \int_\Gamma \frac{f(z)}{(z - \alpha)^2} \, dz.$$

$$\frac{d}{d\alpha}((z - \alpha)^{-1})$$
$$= -(z - \alpha)^{-2} \cdot (-1)$$
$$= (z - \alpha)^{-2}.$$

We get the right answer, but the reasoning is faulty since we cannot just 'differentiate under the integral sign' without justification. We give a correct proof at the end of this subsection.

The formal statement is as follows.

Theorem 3.1 Cauchy's First Derivative Formula

Let $\mathcal{R}$ be a simply-connected region, let Γ be a simple-closed contour in $\mathcal{R}$, and let f be a function which is analytic on $\mathcal{R}$. Then

$$f'(\alpha) = \frac{1}{2\pi i} \int_\Gamma \frac{f(z)}{(z - \alpha)^2} \, dz,$$

for any point α inside Γ.

As with the Integral Formula, we can use the First Derivative Formula to evaluate certain integrals — those with square factors in their denominators — by writing

$$\int_\Gamma \frac{f(z)}{(z-\alpha)^2}\,dz = 2\pi i\, f'(\alpha).$$

We give two examples of this.

Example 3.1

Evaluate $\displaystyle\int_\Gamma \frac{z e^z}{(z-1)^2}\,dz$, where Γ is the circle $\{z : |z| = 2\}$.

Solution

We use Cauchy's First Derivative Formula with $f(z) = z e^z$, $\alpha = 1$, and $\mathcal{R} = \mathbb{C}$. Then $\mathcal{R}$ is simply-connected, Γ is a simple-closed contour in $\mathcal{R}$, and α lies inside Γ (see Figure 3.1). Also, f is analytic on $\mathcal{R}$.

It follows from the First Derivative Formula that

$$\int_\Gamma \frac{z e^z}{(z-1)^2}\,dz = 2\pi i\, f'(1).$$

But $f'(z) = e^z + z e^z$, so $f'(1) = 2e$. Thus

$$\int_\Gamma \frac{z e^z}{(z-1)^2}\,dz = 4\pi e i. \quad\blacksquare$$

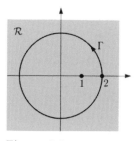

Figure 3.1

In the next example we use partial fractions before applying Cauchy's Integral and First Derivative Formulas.

Example 3.2

Evaluate $\displaystyle\int_\Gamma \frac{4\cos z}{z(z+2)^2}\,dz$, where Γ is the circle $\{z : |z+1| = 3\}$.

Solution

First we express $4/(z(z+2)^2)$ in partial fractions

$$\frac{4}{z(z+2)^2} = \frac{A}{z} + \frac{B}{z+2} + \frac{C}{(z+2)^2},$$

where A, B and C are complex constants. Multiplying both sides by $z(z+2)^2$, we obtain

$$4 = A(z+2)^2 + Bz(z+2) + Cz.$$

Comparing the coefficients of z^2, z and constants, we obtain

$$0 = A + B, \quad 0 = 4A + 2B + C \quad \text{and} \quad 4 = 4A,$$

which can be solved to give $A = 1$, $B = -1$, $C = -2$. Thus

$$\frac{4}{z(z+2)^2} = \frac{1}{z} - \frac{1}{z+2} - \frac{2}{(z+2)^2},$$

and so

$$\int_\Gamma \frac{4\cos z}{z(z+2)^2}\,dz = \int_\Gamma \frac{\cos z}{z}\,dz - \int_\Gamma \frac{\cos z}{z+2}\,dz - 2\int_\Gamma \frac{\cos z}{(z+2)^2}\,dz.$$

We now use Cauchy's Integral Formula and First Derivative Formula with $f(z) = \cos z$, $\alpha = 0$ and -2, and $\mathcal{R} = \mathbb{C}$. Then $\mathcal{R}$ is simply-connected, Γ is a simple-closed contour in $\mathcal{R}$, and α lies inside Γ for both values of α (see Figure 3.2). Also, f is analytic on $\mathcal{R}$.

Note that the repeated factor $(z+2)^2$ in $z(z+2)^2$ leads to the two terms $B/(z+2)$ and $C/(z+2)^2$. In general, a factor $(z+\alpha)^n$ in the denominator leads to the n terms
$$\frac{A_1}{z+\alpha}, \frac{A_2}{(z+\alpha)^2}, \ldots, \frac{A_n}{(z+\alpha)^n},$$
some of which may turn out to be zero.

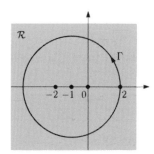

Figure 3.2

It follows from Cauchy's Integral Formula that

$$\int_\Gamma \frac{\cos z}{z}\, dz = 2\pi i \cos 0 = 2\pi i$$

and

$$\int_\Gamma \frac{\cos z}{z+2}\, dz = 2\pi i \cos(-2) = 2\pi i \cos 2,$$

and from Cauchy's First Derivative Formula that

$$\int_\Gamma \frac{\cos z}{(z+2)^2}\, dz = 2\pi i\, f'(-2)$$
$$= 2\pi i(-\sin(-2)) = 2\pi i \sin 2.$$

Putting all this together, we obtain

$$\int_\Gamma \frac{4\cos z}{z(z+2)^2}\, dz = 2\pi i\,(1 - \cos 2 - 2\sin 2). \quad \blacksquare$$

Problem 3.1

Evaluate the integrals

(a) $\displaystyle \int_\Gamma \frac{e^{2z}}{(z+1)^2}\, dz,$ (b) $\displaystyle \int_\Gamma \frac{e^{2z}}{z(z+1)^2}\, dz,$

where Γ is the circle $\{z : |z| = 3\}$.

We now present a proof of Cauchy's First Derivative Formula.

Proof of Cauchy's First Derivative Formula

There are four steps in the proof.

(a) Consider the integral

$$I = \frac{1}{2\pi i} \int_\Gamma \frac{f(z)}{(z-\alpha)^2}\, dz.$$

By the Shrinking Contour Theorem (Theorem 1.4), we can replace Γ by a circle C, with centre α and radius r, lying inside Γ. Thus

$$I = \frac{1}{2\pi i} \int_C \frac{f(z)}{(z-\alpha)^2}\, dz.$$

To prove that $I = f'(\alpha)$, we need to show that

$$\lim_{h \to 0} \frac{1}{h}(f(\alpha + h) - f(\alpha)) = I;$$

that is,

$$\lim_{h \to 0} \frac{1}{h}(f(\alpha + h) - f(\alpha)) - I = 0.$$

This proof may be omitted on a first reading.

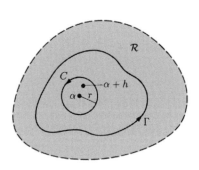

Figure 3.3

(b) Since we are going to let $h \to 0$, we can assume that $\alpha + h$ lies inside C (see Figure 3.3), so that $|h| < r$. Thus, by Cauchy's Integral Formula, we have

$$f(\alpha) = \frac{1}{2\pi i} \int_C \frac{f(z)}{z-\alpha}\, dz \quad \text{and} \quad f(\alpha + h) = \frac{1}{2\pi i} \int_C \frac{f(z)}{z-(\alpha+h)}\, dz.$$

It follows that

$$\frac{1}{h}(f(\alpha + h) - f(\alpha)) - I$$
$$= \frac{1}{2\pi i} \int_C \left(\frac{1}{h}\left(\frac{1}{z-\alpha-h} - \frac{1}{z-\alpha} \right) - \frac{1}{(z-\alpha)^2} \right) f(z)\, dz$$
$$= \frac{1}{2\pi i} \int_C \left(\frac{h}{(z-\alpha-h)(z-\alpha)^2} \right) f(z)\, dz,$$

after simplification.

(c) We now use the Estimation Theorem to give an upper estimate for the modulus of this last integral.

For all z on C, we have $|z - \alpha| = r$ and so, by the backwards form of the Triangle Inequality,

$$|z - \alpha - h| \geq |z - \alpha| - |h| = r - |h|, \qquad \text{for } z \in C.$$

Also, since f is continuous on $\mathcal{R}$, it follows from the Boundedness Theorem that, for some number K,

Unit A3, Theorem 5.3

$$|f(z)| \leq K, \qquad \text{for } z \in C.$$

Thus

$$\left| \frac{h}{(z - \alpha - h)(z - \alpha)^2} f(z) \right| \leq \frac{|h|K}{(r - |h|)r^2}, \qquad \text{for } z \in C.$$

It follows from the Estimation Theorem, with $M = |h|K/((r - |h|)r^2)$ and $L = 2\pi r$, that

$$\begin{aligned}
\left| \frac{1}{2\pi i} \int_C \left(\frac{h}{(z - \alpha - h)(z - \alpha)^2} \right) f(z)\, dz \right| &\leq \frac{1}{2\pi} \cdot \frac{|h|K}{(r - |h|)r^2} \cdot 2\pi r \\
&= \frac{|h|K}{r(r - |h|)}.
\end{aligned}$$

(d) It follows from Steps (b) and (c) that

$$\left| \frac{1}{h}(f(\alpha + h) - f(\alpha)) - I \right| \leq \frac{|h|K}{r(r - |h|)}.$$

Since

$$\lim_{h \to 0} \frac{|h|K}{r(r - |h|)} = 0,$$

we deduce that

$$\lim_{h \to 0} \frac{1}{h}(f(\alpha + h) - f(\alpha)) - I = 0,$$

Here, we are using a 'Squeeze Rule for limits', similar to the Squeeze Rule for null sequences.

as required. ∎

3.2 Cauchy's nth Derivative Formula

We have just seen that, starting from Cauchy's Integral Formula for an analytic function, we can derive another contour integral which gives an expression for the first derivative f'. It is natural to ask whether we can repeat the procedure and derive an expression (involving an integral) for each of the higher derivatives, if these exist.

In order to discover such a formula, let us again throw rigour to the winds, and differentiate the right-hand side of Cauchy's Integral Formula n times with respect to α:

$$\begin{aligned}
\frac{d^n}{d\alpha^n} \left(\frac{1}{2\pi i} \int_\Gamma \frac{f(z)}{z - \alpha}\, dz \right) &= \frac{1}{2\pi i} \int_\Gamma \frac{d^n}{d\alpha^n} \left(\frac{1}{z - \alpha} \right) f(z)\, dz \\
&= \frac{1}{2\pi i} \int_\Gamma \frac{n!}{(z - \alpha)^{n+1}} f(z)\, dz.
\end{aligned}$$

$$\begin{aligned}
\frac{d^n}{d\alpha^n}((z - \alpha)^{-1}) &= \frac{d^{n-1}}{d\alpha^{n-1}}((z - \alpha)^{-2}) \\
&= \frac{d^{n-2}}{d\alpha^{n-2}}(2(z - \alpha)^{-3}) \\
&= \cdots \\
&= n!(z - \alpha)^{-(n+1)}
\end{aligned}$$

This leads to the formula

$$f^{(n)}(\alpha) = \frac{n!}{2\pi i} \int_\Gamma \frac{f(z)}{(z - \alpha)^{n+1}}\, dz.$$

A proof that this formula does hold for $n = 2, 3, \ldots$, can be given along the same lines as the method for proving Cauchy's First Derivative Formula, using Mathematical Induction. The details are more complicated, however, and in *Unit B3* we shall be able to deduce this formula from Taylor's Theorem. At this stage, therefore, we just state Cauchy's nth Derivative Formula and give some of its applications.

Theorem 3.2 Cauchy's nth Derivative Formula

Let $\mathcal{R}$ be a simply-connected region, let Γ be a simple-closed contour in $\mathcal{R}$, and let f be a function which is analytic on $\mathcal{R}$. Then, for any point α inside Γ, f is n-times differentiable at α and

$$f^{(n)}(\alpha) = \frac{n!}{2\pi i} \int_\Gamma \frac{f(z)}{(z-\alpha)^{n+1}}\, dz, \qquad \text{for } n = 1, 2, \ldots .$$

It is often convenient to refer to Cauchy's First Derivative Formula, Cauchy's Second Derivative Formula, ... See the solution to Problem 3.2(c), for example.

We can now evaluate integrals with higher powers of linear factors in their denominators, by writing the nth Derivative Formula in the form

$$\int_\Gamma \frac{f(z)}{(z-\alpha)^{n+1}}\, dz = 2\pi i \frac{f^{(n)}(\alpha)}{n!}.$$

Example 3.3

Evaluate the integral

$$\int_\Gamma \frac{z \sin z}{(z - \pi/4)^3}\, dz,$$

where Γ is the square contour with vertices $2 + 2i$, $-2 + 2i$, $-2 - 2i$, $2 - 2i$.

Solution

We use Cauchy's nth Derivative Formula with $n = 2$, $f(z) = z \sin z$, $\alpha = \pi/4$, and $\mathcal{R} = \mathbb{C}$. Then $\mathcal{R}$ is simply-connected, Γ is a simple-closed contour in $\mathcal{R}$, and α lies inside Γ (see Figure 3.4). Also, f is analytic on $\mathcal{R}$.

It follows from the nth Derivative Formula that

$$\int_\Gamma \frac{z \sin z}{(z - \pi/4)^3}\, dz = 2\pi i \frac{f''(\pi/4)}{2!}.$$

But $f'(z) = \sin z + z \cos z$, and $f''(z) = 2 \cos z - z \sin z$, so

$$f''(\pi/4) = 2\cos(\pi/4) - (\pi/4)\sin(\pi/4) = (2 - \pi/4)/\sqrt{2}.$$

Thus

$$\int_\Gamma \frac{z \sin z}{(z - \pi/4)^3}\, dz = \sqrt{2}\pi(1 - \pi/8)i. \quad \blacksquare$$

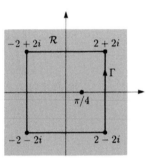

Figure 3.4

Problem 3.2

Evaluate

(a) $\displaystyle\int_\Gamma \frac{\cosh 2z}{(z+i)^3}\, dz$,   (b) $\displaystyle\int_\Gamma \frac{ze^z}{(z-1)^{10}}\, dz$,   (c) $\displaystyle\int_\Gamma \frac{e^{2z}}{z^3(z+1)}\, dz$,

where Γ is the circle $\{z : |z| = 2\}$.

The method of evaluating integrals of the type in Example 3.3 and Problem 3.2 is developed in a strategy given in Section 4. In the next problem we ask you to prove a result which will be needed later in the course.

Problem 3.3

Let $\mathcal{R}$ be a simply-connected region containing the circle $\Gamma = \{z : |z - \alpha| = r\}$. Let f be a function which is analytic on $\mathcal{R}$, and suppose that

$$|f(z)| \leq K, \qquad \text{for } z \in \Gamma.$$

Use the Estimation Theorem to prove that, for any $n \geq 1$,

$$|f^{(n)}(\alpha)| \leq Kn!/r^n.$$

This result is called **Cauchy's Estimate**.

Cauchy's nth Derivative Formula is evidently a useful tool for evaluating certain types of contour integrals. However, the greater significance of this result lies in the fact that if f is analytic on a region $\mathcal{R}$, then it has derivatives of all orders at any point α in $\mathcal{R}$.

Theorem 3.3 Analyticity of Derivatives

Let $\mathcal{R}$ be a region, and let f be a function which is analytic on $\mathcal{R}$. Then f possesses derivatives of all orders on $\mathcal{R}$, so that f', f'', $f^{(3)}, \ldots$ are analytic on $\mathcal{R}$.

Note that $\mathcal{R}$ is *not* assumed to be simply-connected in this result.

Proof Let α be any point of $\mathcal{R}$, let D be an open disc with centre α lying in $\mathcal{R}$, and let Γ be any circle with centre α lying in D. Then $f^{(n)}(\alpha)$ exists for $n = 1, 2, \ldots$, and is given by the nth Derivative Formula. ∎

Such a disc exists, as $\mathcal{R}$ is an open set.

Note that the corresponding assertion for real functions does not hold. For example, consider the differentiable function

$$f(x) = \begin{cases} x^2, & x \geq 0, \\ -x^2, & x < 0. \end{cases}$$

Then $f'(x) = 2|x|$, and so f' is not differentiable at 0 (see Figure 3.5).

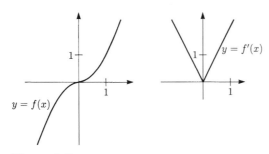

$y = f(x)$

$y = f'(x)$

Figure 3.5

Problem 3.4

Use the Analyticity of Derivatives to prove the following propositions.

(a) There is no analytic function F such that

$$F'(z) = |z|, \qquad \text{for all } z \in \mathbb{C}.$$

(b) If f is an entire function such that f' is bounded, then f is a linear function; that is,

$$f(z) = \alpha z + \beta, \qquad \text{where } \alpha, \beta \in \mathbb{C}.$$

4 REVISION (AUDIO-TAPE)

After working through this section, you should be able to:

(a) identify and use appropriate techniques for evaluating various contour integrals;

(b) use contour integrals to evaluate various *real* integrals.

In the audio-tape frames you will see examples of the following techniques for evaluating integrals.

Parametrization

Let $\Gamma : \gamma(t)$ ($t \in [a, b]$) be a smooth path in $\mathbb{C}$, and let f be a function which is continuous on Γ. Then, by definition,

Unit B1, Section 2

$$\int_\Gamma f(z)\,dz = \int_a^b f(\gamma(t))\gamma'(t)\,dt.$$

The integral of f along a contour is the sum of the integrals of f along its constituent smooth paths.

Closed Contour Theorem

Let the function f be continuous and have a primitive F on a region $\mathcal{R}$. Then

Unit B1, Theorem 3.4

$$\int_\Gamma f(z)\,dz = 0, \quad \text{for any closed contour } \Gamma \text{ in } \mathcal{R}.$$

Cauchy's Theorem

Let $\mathcal{R}$ be a simply-connected region, and let f be a function which is analytic on $\mathcal{R}$. Then

Theorem 1.2

$$\int_\Gamma f(z)\,dz = 0, \quad \text{for any closed contour } \Gamma \text{ in } \mathcal{R}.$$

Cauchy's Integral Formula

Let $\mathcal{R}$ be a simply-connected region, let Γ be a simple-closed contour in $\mathcal{R}$, and let f be a function which is analytic on $\mathcal{R}$. Then

Theorem 2.1

$$f(\alpha) = \frac{1}{2\pi i} \int_\Gamma \frac{f(z)}{z - \alpha}\,dz, \quad \text{for any point } \alpha \text{ inside } \Gamma.$$

Cauchy's *n*th Derivative Formula

Let $\mathcal{R}$ be a simply-connected region, let Γ be a simple-closed contour in $\mathcal{R}$, and let f be a function which is analytic on $\mathcal{R}$. Then, for any point α inside Γ, f is n-times differentiable at α and

Theorem 3.2

$$f^{(n)}(\alpha) = \frac{n!}{2\pi i} \int_\Gamma \frac{f(z)}{(z - \alpha)^{n+1}}\,dz, \quad \text{for } n = 1, 2, \ldots.$$

Before starting the tape, you should attempt the following problem on partial fractions; the results will be needed in the audio tape.

Problem 4.1

Expand each of the following expressions as partial fractions.

(a) $\dfrac{1}{z(z - 3)}$ (b) $\dfrac{1}{z^2(z - 3)}$ (c) $\dfrac{1}{z^3(z - 3)}$

NOW START THE TAPE.

28

1. Evaluate $\int_\Gamma \frac{1}{z}\, dz$, $\Gamma=\{z:|z|=1\}$

Parametrization

$\gamma(t)=e^{it}$ $(t\in[0,2\pi])$.

Thus

$$\int_\Gamma \frac{1}{z}\, dz = \int_0^{2\pi} e^{-it}\, i e^{it}\, dt$$
$$= \int_0^{2\pi} i\, dt = 2\pi i.$$

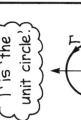

Γ is 'the unit circle'.

$\gamma'(t)=ie^{it}$

2. Evaluate $\int_\Gamma \frac{1}{z+2}\, dz$, $\Gamma=\{z:|z|=1\}$

Parametrization — *see Frame 10.*

Cauchy's Theorem

$f(z)=\frac{1}{z+2}$ is analytic on $\mathcal{R}=\{z:\operatorname{Re}z > -\tfrac{3}{2}\}$.

Hence

$$\int_\Gamma f(z)\, dz = \int_\Gamma \frac{1}{z+2}\, dz = 0.$$

Closed Contour Theorem

f has primitive $F(z)=\mathrm{Log}(z+2)$ on $\mathcal{R}$, so

$$\int_\Gamma f(z)\, dz = \int_\Gamma \frac{1}{z+2}\, dz = 0.$$

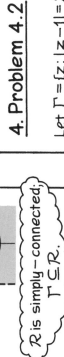

$\mathcal{R}$ is simply-connected; $\Gamma \subseteq \mathcal{R}$.

F is analytic on $\mathbb{C}-\{x\in\mathbb{R}: x\le -2\}$.

$$\int_\Gamma \frac{1}{z-\alpha}\, dz = 0,\ \text{for}\ \alpha\ \text{outside}\ \Gamma.$$

3. Evaluate $\int_\Gamma \frac{1}{z-\frac{1}{2}}\, dz$, $\Gamma=\{z:|z|=1\}$

Parametrization— *see Frame 11.*

Cauchy's Theorem — not applicable :

$f(z)=\frac{1}{z-\frac{1}{2}}$ is not analytic on a simply-connected region $\mathcal{R}$ containing Γ.

Cauchy's Integral Formula

$f(z)=1$ is analytic on $\mathcal{R}=\mathbb{C}$, $\Gamma\subseteq\mathcal{R}$, $\alpha=\frac{1}{2}$ is inside Γ; so

$$\int_\Gamma \frac{1}{z-\frac{1}{2}}\, dz = \int_\Gamma \frac{f(z)}{z-\frac{1}{2}}\, dz$$
$$= 2\pi i\, f(\tfrac{1}{2}) = 2\pi i.$$

$$f(\alpha)=\frac{1}{2\pi i}\int_\Gamma \frac{f(z)}{z-\alpha}\, dz$$

$$\int_\Gamma \frac{1}{z-\alpha}\, dz = 2\pi i,\quad \text{for}\ \alpha\ \text{inside}\ \Gamma.$$

4. Problem 4.2

Let $\Gamma=\{z:|z-1|=2\}$.

Evaluate each of the following integrals.

(a) $\int_\Gamma \frac{1}{z}\, dz$ (b) $\int_\Gamma \frac{1}{z-5}\, dz$ (c) $\int_\Gamma \frac{1}{(z-1)^2}\, dz$

5. Evaluate $I = \int_\Gamma \frac{e^z}{z(z^2-9)}\,dz$, $\Gamma=\{z:|z-2|=3\}$

Integrand is analytic except at $0, 3$ (inside Γ) and -3 (outside Γ).

Hence choose

$$f(z) = \frac{e^z}{z+3},$$

which is analytic on

$$\mathcal{R} = \{z: \operatorname{Re} z > -3\}.$$

Also

$$\frac{1}{z(z-3)} = \frac{1/3}{z-3} - \frac{1/3}{z}.$$

Thus

$$I = \int_\Gamma \frac{f(z)}{z(z-3)}\,dz$$

$$= \frac{1}{3}\int_\Gamma \frac{f(z)}{z-3}\,dz - \frac{1}{3}\int_\Gamma \frac{f(z)}{z}\,dz$$

$$= \frac{1}{3}\,2\pi i\, f(3) - \frac{1}{3}\,2\pi i\, f(0)$$

$$= \frac{1}{3}\,2\pi i\, \frac{e^3}{6} - \frac{1}{3}\,2\pi i\, \frac{e^0}{3}$$

$$= \frac{\pi i}{9}\,(e^3 - 2).$$

> $\mathcal{R}$ is simply-connected; $\Gamma \subseteq \mathcal{R}$.

> partial fractions

> two terms in denominator

> Cauchy's Integral Formula:
> $$f(\alpha) = \frac{1}{2\pi i}\int_\Gamma \frac{f(z)}{z-\alpha}\,dz.$$

6. Evaluate $I = \int_\Gamma \frac{e^z}{z^2(z^2-9)}\,dz$, $\Gamma=\{z:|z-2|=3\}$

Again choose

$$f(z) = \frac{e^z}{z+3},$$

which is analytic on $\mathcal{R} = \{z: \operatorname{Re} z > -3\}$.

Also

$$\frac{1}{z^2(z-3)} = \frac{1/9}{z-3} - \frac{1/9}{z} - \frac{1/3}{z^2}.$$

Thus

$$I = \int_\Gamma \frac{f(z)}{z^2(z-3)}\,dz$$

$$= \frac{1}{9}\int_\Gamma \frac{f(z)}{z-3}\,dz - \frac{1}{9}\int_\Gamma \frac{f(z)}{z}\,dz - \frac{1}{3}\int_\Gamma \frac{f(z)}{z^2}\,dz$$

$$= \frac{1}{9}\,2\pi i\, f(3) - \frac{1}{9}\,2\pi i\, f(0) - \frac{1}{3}\,2\pi i\, f'(0)$$

$$= \frac{1}{9}\,2\pi i\, \frac{e^3}{6} - \frac{1}{9}\,2\pi i\, \frac{e^0}{3} - \frac{1}{3}\,2\pi i\, \left(\frac{2}{9}\right)$$

$$= \frac{\pi i}{27}\,(e^3 - 6).$$

> partial fractions

> Cauchy's First Derivative Formula:
> $$f'(\alpha) = \frac{1}{2\pi i}\int_\Gamma \frac{f(z)}{(z-\alpha)^2}\,dz.$$

> See Problem 4.1 for partial fractions.

7. Problem 4.3

Evaluate $\int_\Gamma \frac{e^z}{z^3(z^2-9)}\,dz$, $\Gamma=\{z:|z-2|=3\}$.

8. Strategy.

> • g is analytic on a simply-connected region, containing Γ;
> • Γ, a simple-closed contour;
> • p is a polynomial function with no zeros on Γ.

To evaluate

$$I = \int_\Gamma \frac{g(z)}{p(z)}\, dz:$$

(a) factorize $p(z) = q(z)\, r(z)$, with zeros of $\begin{cases} q \text{ inside } \Gamma, \\ r \text{ outside } \Gamma; \end{cases}$

zeros of q

zeros of r

then $f = g/r$ is analytic on a simply-connected region $\mathcal{R}$ which contains Γ but not the zeros of r.

(b) expand $1/q(z)$ in partial fractions;

(c) hence expand $I = \int_\Gamma \frac{f(z)}{q(z)}\, dz$

as a sum of integrals, which can be evaluated using Cauchy's formulas.

9. Problem 4.4

Use the above strategy to evaluate each of the following integrals, where $\Gamma = \{z : |z - i/2| = 3/4\}$.

(a) $\displaystyle\int_\Gamma \frac{e^{2z}}{z(z^2+1)}\, dz$ (b) $\displaystyle\int_\Gamma \frac{e^{2z}}{z^2(z^2+1)}\, dz$

10. Evaluating real integrals

From Frame 2,

$$\int_\Gamma \frac{1}{z+2}\, dz = 0, \quad \Gamma = \{z : |z| = 1\}.$$

> Cauchy's Theorem

The standard parametrization $8(t) = e^{it}$ ($t \in [0, 2\pi]$) gives

$$0 = \int_0^{2\pi} \frac{1}{e^{it}+2}\, ie^{it}\, dt$$

$$= \int_0^{2\pi} \frac{e^{-it}+2}{(e^{it}+2)(e^{-it}+2)}\, ie^{it}\, dt$$

$$= \int_0^{2\pi} \frac{i+2ie^{it}}{5+2(e^{it}+e^{-it})}\, dt$$

$$= \int_0^{2\pi} \frac{-2\sin t}{5+4\cos t}\, dt + i\int_0^{2\pi} \frac{1+2\cos t}{5+4\cos t}\, dt.$$

> $e^{it} = \cos t + i\sin t$
> $e^{it} + e^{-it}$
> $= 2\cos t$

So $\displaystyle\int_0^{2\pi} \frac{-2\sin t}{5+4\cos t}\, dt = 0,$ $\displaystyle\int_0^{2\pi} \frac{1+2\cos t}{5+4\cos t}\, dt = 0.$

11. Problem 4.5

By considering

$$\int_\Gamma \frac{1}{z-\frac{1}{2}}\, dz, \quad \Gamma = \{z : |z| = 1\},$$

evaluate two real integrals.

> Frame 3

5 THE PROOF OF CAUCHY'S THEOREM

After working through this section, you should be able to:

(a) understand the proof of Cauchy's Theorem;

(b) state Morera's Theorem.

In Section 1 we outlined the proof of Cauchy's Theorem (Theorem 1.2). We now expand this outline to a full proof.

A key ingredient in the proof is the Nested Rectangles Theorem. We state it here for convenience.

Unit A3, Theorem 5.6

Nested Rectangles Theorem

Let $R_n, n = 0, 1, 2, \ldots$, be a sequence of closed rectangles with sides parallel to the axes, and with diagonals of lengths $s_n, n = 0, 1, 2, \ldots$, such that

1. $R_0 \supseteq R_1 \supseteq R_2 \supseteq \ldots$, and

2. $\lim\limits_{n \to \infty} s_n = 0$.

Then there is a unique complex number α which lies in all of the rectangles R_n. Moreover, for each positive number ε, there is an integer N such that

$$R_n \subseteq \{z : |z - \alpha| < \varepsilon\}, \qquad \text{for all } n > N.$$

5.1 Cauchy's Theorem for a rectangular contour

In this subsection, we give the first stage of the proof of Cauchy's Theorem — the special case when Γ is a rectangular contour in $\mathcal{R}$ (see Figure 5.1). This special case is in fact due to Goursat. Earlier proofs of Cauchy's Theorem had made the unnecessary assumption that the derivative of f is a continuous function.

Edouard Goursat (1858–1936) was a French mathematician, who made contributions to refining Cauchy's Theorem.

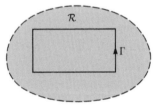

Figure 5.1

Theorem 5.1 Cauchy's Theorem for a Rectangular Contour

Let $\mathcal{R}$ be a simply-connected region, and let f be a function which is analytic on $\mathcal{R}$. Then

$$\int_\Gamma f(z)\,dz = 0,$$

for any rectangular contour Γ in $\mathcal{R}$.

Proof There are four steps in this proof.

This proof may be omitted on a first reading.

Let

$$I = \int_\Gamma f(z)\, dz,$$

where Γ is a rectangular contour.

(a) We first construct a sequence $\Delta_0, \Delta_1, \Delta_2, \ldots$, of rectangular contours in $\mathcal{R}$, such that

$$|I| \le 4^n \left| \int_{\Delta_n} f(z)\, dz \right|, \qquad \text{for } n = 0, 1, 2, \ldots.$$

To begin, let $\Delta_0 = \Gamma$.

We use the Greek capital letter delta, Δ, to label these contours because Γ is already in use.

In order to construct Δ_1, we split the interior of Γ into four congruent rectangles with boundary contours Γ_1, Γ_2, Γ_3 and Γ_4, the vertices of which are labelled O, A, B, C, D, E, F, G and H (see Figure 5.2).

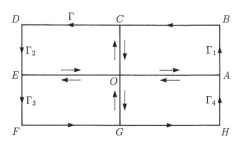

Figure 5.2 $\Gamma_1 : OABCO$, $\Gamma_2 : OCDEO$, $\Gamma_3 : OEFGO$, $\Gamma_4 : OGHAO$

Consider

$$\int_{\Gamma_1} f(z)\, dz + \int_{\Gamma_2} f(z)\, dz + \int_{\Gamma_3} f(z)\, dz + \int_{\Gamma_4} f(z)\, dz.$$

Since

$$\int_{OA} f(z)\, dz = - \int_{AO} f(z)\, dz, \qquad \int_{OC} f(z)\, dz = - \int_{CO} f(z)\, dz,$$

$$\int_{OE} f(z)\, dz = - \int_{EO} f(z)\, dz, \qquad \int_{OG} f(z)\, dz = - \int_{GO} f(z)\, dz,$$

we deduce that

Here, for example,

$$\int_{OA} f(z)\, dz$$

denotes the integral of f along the line segment from O to A.

$$\int_{\Gamma_1} f(z)\, dz + \int_{\Gamma_2} f(z)\, dz + \int_{\Gamma_3} f(z)\, dz + \int_{\Gamma_4} f(z)\, dz = I,$$

and so, by the Triangle Inequality,

$$|I| \le \left| \int_{\Gamma_1} f(z)\, dz \right| + \left| \int_{\Gamma_2} f(z)\, dz \right| + \left| \int_{\Gamma_3} f(z)\, dz \right| + \left| \int_{\Gamma_4} f(z)\, dz \right|.$$

Now let k be such that $\left| \int_{\Gamma_k} f(z)\, dz \right|$ is the largest of the four terms on the right, and let $\Delta_1 = \Gamma_k$; if more than one integral has the same largest modulus, let Δ_1 be any one of them. Then

$$|I| \le 4 \left| \int_{\Delta_1} f(z)\, dz \right|.$$

Note that, if the original contour Γ has length l, then the length of the new contour Δ_1 is $\frac{1}{2}l$; we write $L(\Delta_1) = \frac{1}{2}l$.

To sum up, we have chosen Δ_1 such that

$$|I| \le 4 \left| \int_{\Delta_1} f(z)\, dz \right| \quad \text{and} \quad L(\Delta_1) = \tfrac{1}{2}l. \tag{5.1}$$

We now repeat the above argument with Δ_1 instead of Γ; we split the interior of Δ_1 into four congruent rectangles, and let Δ_2 be the boundary of one of these, chosen so that the integral around it has the largest modulus:

Figure 5.3 shows an example of this, with $\Delta_1 = \Gamma_1$. Hence, as before,

$$\left| \int_{\Delta_1} f(z)\, dz \right| \le 4 \left| \int_{\Delta_2} f(z)\, dz \right|.$$

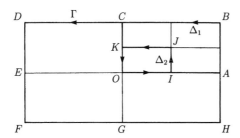

Figure 5.3 $\Gamma : BDFHB$, $\Delta_1 : OABCO$, $\Delta_2 : OIJKO$

Also, the length of Δ_2 is one-half of the length of Δ_1; that is, $L(\Delta_2) = \frac{1}{2} L(\Delta_1)$. Combining these results with those of Equation (5.1), we obtain

$$|I| \le 4^2 \left| \int_{\Delta_2} f(z)\, dz \right| \quad \text{and} \quad L(\Delta_2) = \tfrac{1}{4} l.$$

We now repeat the argument indefinitely to produce a sequence of nested rectangular contours Δ_n, $n = 0, 1, 2, \ldots$, such that

$$|I| \le 4^n \left| \int_{\Delta_n} f(z)\, dz \right| \tag{5.2}$$

and

$$L(\Delta_n) = l/2^n. \tag{5.3}$$

(b) Next we use the Nested Rectangles Theorem. For $n = 0, 1, 2, \ldots$, let R_n be the closed rectangle consisting of Δ_n and its inside. Then

Figure 5.4 Rectangle R_n

1. $R_0 \supseteq R_1 \supseteq R_2 \supseteq \ldots$.

Also, for each rectangle R_n, the length s_n of its diagonal (see Figure 5.4) satisfies

$$0 \le s_n \le L(\Delta_n);$$

since $\lim\limits_{n \to \infty} L(\Delta_n) = \lim\limits_{n \to \infty} l/2^n = 0$, it follows from the Squeeze Rule for sequences that

2. $\lim\limits_{n \to \infty} s_n = 0$.

It follows from the Nested Rectangles Theorem that there is a unique complex number α which lies in all of the rectangles R_n (see Figure 5.5).

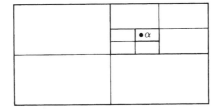

Figure 5.5 $\alpha \in R_n, n = 0, 1, 2, \ldots$

(c) We now use the fact that f is an analytic function. Since f is analytic on $\mathcal{R}$, f is differentiable at α; that is,

$$\lim_{z \to \alpha} \frac{f(z) - f(\alpha)}{z - \alpha} = f'(\alpha).$$

Thus

$$\frac{f(z) - f(\alpha)}{z - \alpha} = f'(\alpha) + r(z), \quad \text{where } \lim_{z \to \alpha} r(z) = 0,$$

which can be written in the form

$$f(z) = f(\alpha) + f'(\alpha)(z - \alpha) + (z - \alpha)r(z).$$

Integrating around Δ_n, we obtain

$$\int_{\Delta_n} f(z)\, dz = \int_{\Delta_n} (f(\alpha) + f'(\alpha)(z - \alpha))\, dz + \int_{\Delta_n} (z - \alpha)r(z)\, dz.$$

Now, the first integral on the right-hand side is 0 since the integrand is a polynomial, and so the Closed Contour Theorem can be applied.

Thus

$$\int_{\Delta_n} f(z)\, dz = \int_{\Delta_n} (z - \alpha)r(z)\, dz.$$

(d) Finally, we apply the Estimation Theorem to the previous integral.

Unit B1, Theorem 4.1

The length of the contour is no problem: by Equation (5.3), we have $L = l/2^n$.

Now suppose that $\varepsilon > 0$ is given. Since

$$\lim_{z \to \alpha} r(z) = 0,$$

we know that there is a $\delta > 0$ such that

$$|z - \alpha| < \delta \quad \Longrightarrow \quad |r(z)| < \varepsilon.$$

We now choose N in such a way that, for $n > N$, the contour Δ_n lies entirely within the disc $\{z : |z - \alpha| < \delta\}$. Thus, for $z \in \Delta_n$, we have

See the final statement of the Nested Rectangles Theorem.

$$|(z - \alpha)r(z)| = |z - \alpha||r(z)| < (l/2^n)\varepsilon \quad (\text{since } |z - \alpha| < s_n).$$

It follows, on applying the Estimation Theorem with $M = (l/2^n)\varepsilon$ and $L = l/2^n$, that

$$\left| \int_{\Delta_n} f(z)\, dz \right| = \left| \int_{\Delta_n} (z - \alpha)r(z)\, dz \right| \le \frac{l\varepsilon}{2^n} \times \frac{l}{2^n} = \frac{l^2\varepsilon}{4^n}.$$

Hence, by Inequality (5.2),

$$|I| \le 4^n \left| \int_{\Delta_n} f(z)\, dz \right| \le 4^n \times \frac{l^2\varepsilon}{4^n} = l^2\varepsilon.$$

Since $|I| \le l^2\varepsilon$ for any positive ε, we have

$$I = 0. \quad \blacksquare$$

See Remark 1 in Subsection 2.2.

5.2 Cauchy's Theorem for a closed grid path

The next stage in the proof of Cauchy's Theorem is to prove the theorem for the case of a closed grid path. Recall from the previous unit that a grid path is a contour made up of line segments which are parallel to the x- and y-axes.

Theorem 5.2 Cauchy's Theorem for a Closed Grid Path

Let $\mathcal{R}$ be a simply-connected region, and let f be a function which is analytic on $\mathcal{R}$. Then

$$\int_\Gamma f(z)\, dz = 0,$$

for any closed grid path Γ in $\mathcal{R}$.

Proof Suppose first that Γ is a *simple-closed* grid path, such as the one illustrated on the left in Figure 5.6. Then we can introduce extra horizontal and vertical line segments, as shown on the right in Figure 5.6, to divide the inside of Γ into rectangles $R_1, R_2, \ldots, R_n$, whose interiors are disjoint; for example, this can be done by extending to the inside of Γ all the horizontal and vertical line segments in Γ.

This proof may be omitted on a first reading.

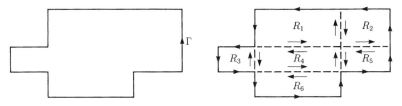

Figure 5.6 Dividing the inside of a simple-closed grid path

Now note that the integral of f around each of the boundaries $\Gamma_1, \Gamma_2, \ldots, \Gamma_n$ of the rectangles $R_1, R_2, \ldots, R_n$ is zero, by Theorem 5.1. So

$$\int_{\Gamma_1} f + \int_{\Gamma_2} f + \cdots + \int_{\Gamma_n} f = 0.$$

Also, as in the proof of Cauchy's Theorem for a rectangular contour, the integral of f along each of the line segments inside Γ occurs twice in this sum of integrals (once in each direction) and so they cancel in pairs. It follows that

$$\int_{\Gamma} f = \int_{\Gamma_1} f + \int_{\Gamma_2} f + \cdots + \int_{\Gamma_n} f = 0,$$

as required.

To complete the proof we note that any *closed* grid path can be decomposed into:

> a finite number of simple-closed grid paths, and
>
> a finite number of line segments, each traversed in both directions.

This fact is illustrated in Figure 5.7.

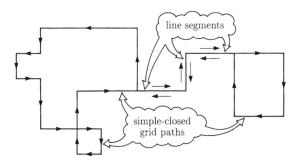

Figure 5.7 A 'decomposed' closed grid path

Since the integral of f around a simple-closed grid path is zero and the integrals of f along the line segments cancel in pairs, we deduce that the integral of f along any closed grid path is zero. ∎

5.3 The Primitive Theorem

In this subsection we present the final stage in our proof of Cauchy's Theorem. We start by proving the Primitive Theorem.

Theorem 5.3 Primitive Theorem (or Antiderivative Theorem)

If a function f is analytic on a simply-connected region $\mathcal{R}$, then f has a primitive on $\mathcal{R}$.

Proof First we introduce the notation

$$\int_\alpha^\beta f(z)\,dz, \qquad \text{for } \alpha, \beta \in \mathcal{R},$$

to denote the integral of f along any grid path in $\mathcal{R}$ from α to β. This notation is well defined here (that is, it does not depend on which grid path from α to β we choose) because if Γ_1 and Γ_2 are both grid paths from α to β, then

$$\int_{\Gamma_1} f(z)\,dz - \int_{\Gamma_2} f(z)\,dz = \int_{\Gamma_1} f(z)\,dz + \int_{\widetilde{\Gamma}_2} f(z)\,dz$$

$$= \int_{\Gamma_1 + \widetilde{\Gamma}_2} f(z)\,dz$$

$$= 0.$$

This proof may be omitted on a first reading.

$\widetilde{\Gamma}_2$ *is the reverse of* Γ_2.

This last equality follows from Theorem 5.2, because $\Gamma_1 + \widetilde{\Gamma}_2$ is a closed grid path in $\mathcal{R}$.

Now choose a point α in $\mathcal{R}$ and define a function $F : \mathcal{R} \longrightarrow \mathbb{C}$ by

$$F(z) = \int_\alpha^z f(w)\,dw \qquad (z \in \mathcal{R}).$$

We claim that

$$F'(z) = f(z), \qquad \text{for } z \in \mathcal{R}, \tag{5.4}$$

so that F is a primitive of f on $\mathcal{R}$.

To prove Equation (5.4), note that if $z + h \in \mathcal{R}$, then

$$\frac{F(z+h) - F(z)}{h} = \frac{1}{h}\left(\int_\alpha^{z+h} f(w)\,dw - \int_\alpha^z f(w)\,dw \right)$$

$$= \frac{1}{h}\int_z^{z+h} f(w)\,dw.$$

This last equality follows by considering a grid path in $\mathcal{R}$ from α to $z+h$ which passes through z, as shown in Figure 5.8. Hence

$$\frac{F(z+h) - F(z)}{h} - f(z) = \frac{1}{h}\int_z^{z+h} (f(w) - f(z))\,dw,$$

since

$$\int_z^{z+h} f(z)\,dw = f(z)\int_z^{z+h} 1\,dw = f(z)h.$$

To complete the proof, we need to show that

$$\lim_{h \to 0} \frac{1}{h}\int_z^{z+h} (f(w) - f(z))\,dw = 0,$$

for then $F'(z) = f(z)$. To do this we suppose that $z + h$ lies in an open disc with centre z in $\mathcal{R}$ (see Figure 5.9) and take a 'simplest possible' grid path Γ in $\mathcal{R}$ from z to $z + h$ (consisting of at most two line segments, see Figure 5.10).

This is the only point in this proof where we need to use the hypothesis that $\mathcal{R}$ is simply-connected.

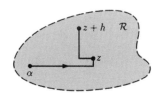

Figure 5.8

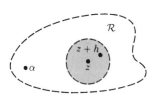

Figure 5.9

Figure 5.10

We now use the Estimation Theorem with

$$L = L(\Gamma) \le 2|h| \quad \text{(see Figure 5.10)}$$

and

$$M = m(h),$$

where $m(h) = \max\{|f(w) - f(z)| : |w - z| \le |h|\}$. We choose this value for M because

$$\max\{|f(w) - f(z)| : w \in \Gamma\} \le \max\{|f(w) - f(z)| : |w - z| \le |h|\};$$

see Figure 5.11. Thus

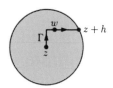

$$\left| \frac{1}{h} \int_z^{z+h} (f(w) - f(z))\, dw \right| \le \frac{1}{|h|} \cdot m(h) \cdot 2|h|$$

$$= 2m(h). \tag{5.5}$$

Since f is differentiable at z, it is continuous there, and thus

$$\lim_{w \to z} f(w) = f(z).$$

Hence the right-hand side of (5.5) tends to zero as $h \to 0$ and so $F'(z) = f(z)$, as required. ∎

At long last we can prove Cauchy's Theorem!

Theorem 1.2 Cauchy's Theorem

Let $\mathcal{R}$ be a simply-connected region, and let f be a function which is analytic on $\mathcal{R}$. Then

$$\int_\Gamma f(z)\, dz = 0,$$

for any closed contour Γ in $\mathcal{R}$.

Proof By Theorem 5.3, f has a primitive on $\mathcal{R}$. Since f is analytic on $\mathcal{R}$, it is continuous on $\mathcal{R}$ and so, by the Closed Contour Theorem (see the Introduction),

$$\int_\Gamma f(z)\, dz = 0,$$

as required. ∎

5.4 Morera's Theorem

In this subsection we state and prove Morera's Theorem, a result which will be used later in the course. As you can see, this theorem is a partial converse to Cauchy's Theorem.

Theorem 5.4 Morera's Theorem

If a function f is continuous on a region $\mathcal{R}$ and

$$\int_\Gamma f(z)\, dz = 0,$$

for all rectangular contours Γ in $\mathcal{R}$, then f is analytic on $\mathcal{R}$.

Giacinto Morera (1856–1909) proved this theorem in 1886.

Proof   The proof of the Primitive Theorem (Theorem 5.3) is essentially a proof of the following result:

This proof may be omitted on a first reading.

if

> f is continuous on a region $\mathcal{R}$,

analytic $\Longrightarrow$ continuous

and

$$\int_\Gamma f(z)\,dz = 0 \text{ for all closed grid paths in } \mathcal{R}, \qquad (5.6)$$

conclusion of Theorem 5.2

> then f has a primitive on $\mathcal{R}$.

The hypothesis in the Primitive Theorem that $\mathcal{R}$ is simply-connected was needed only in order to apply Theorem 5.2.

The hypotheses of Morera's Theorem imply that (5.6) holds (as in the proof of Theorem 5.2). Hence f has a primitive F on $\mathcal{R}$. By the Analyticity of Derivatives, it then follows that the function f $(= F')$ must be analytic on $\mathcal{R}$, as required. ∎

Theorem 3.3

EXERCISES

Section 1

Exercise 1.1 State whether or not each of the following regions is simply-connected. Justify your answers.

(a) $\{z : 2 < |z - 3| < 4\}$ (b) $\{z : |z| > 0\}$ (c) $\{z : -1 < \operatorname{Re} z < 1\}$

(d) $\{z : -\pi < \operatorname{Arg} z < \pi\}$ (e) the domain of the tangent function

Exercise 1.2 State which of the following paths Γ are simple-closed. For those that are not, explain why not.

(a) $\Gamma : \gamma(t) = e^{it}\ (t \in [0, \pi])$ (b) $\Gamma : \gamma(t) = e^{it}\ (t \in [0, 2\pi])$

(c) $\Gamma : \gamma(t) = e^{it}\ (t \in [0, 4\pi])$ (d) $\Gamma : \gamma(t) = te^{it}\ (t \in [0, 2\pi])$

Exercise 1.3 Use Cauchy's Theorem to establish that each of the following integrals along the contour $\Gamma = \{z : |z| = 2\}$ is zero.

(a) $\displaystyle\int_\Gamma \sin z\,dz$ (b) $\displaystyle\int_\Gamma \tan\left(\tfrac{1}{2}z\right) dz$ (c) $\displaystyle\int_\Gamma \frac{1}{z - \pi}\,dz$

(d) $\displaystyle\int_\Gamma \left((z^3 + 3z - 2)e^z + \operatorname{Log}(z + 3i)\right) dz$

Exercise 1.4 Explain why Cauchy's Theorem is not appropriate for evaluating each of the following integrals.

(a) $\displaystyle\int_\Gamma \sec z\,dz$, where $\Gamma = \{z : |z| = 2\}$

(b) $\displaystyle\int_\Gamma \operatorname{Log}(1 + z)\,dz$, where $\Gamma = \{z : |z| = 1\}$

(c) $\displaystyle\int_\Gamma \frac{1}{z - 1}\,dz$, where $\Gamma = \{z : |z| = 3\}$

(d) $\displaystyle\int_\Gamma e^z\,dz$, where Γ has parametrization $\gamma(t) = (1 - t) + it\ (t \in [0, 1])$

Exercise 1.5 Explain why each of the following pairs of integrals I_1 and I_2 has the same value. (Do not evaluate the integrals.)

(a) $I_1 = \displaystyle\int_{\Gamma_1} ze^z\, dz, \quad \Gamma_1 : \gamma_1(t) = it \ (t \in [0,1])$

$\quad I_2 = \displaystyle\int_{\Gamma_2} ze^z\, dz, \quad \Gamma_2 : \gamma_2(t) = \tfrac{1}{2}i + \tfrac{1}{2}e^{it} \ (t \in [-\pi/2, \pi/2])$

(b) $I_1 = \displaystyle\int_{\Gamma_1} \frac{\mathrm{Log}\, z}{z-3}\, dz, \quad \Gamma_1 = \{z : |z-4| = 2\}$

$\quad I_2 = \displaystyle\int_{\Gamma_2} \frac{\mathrm{Log}\, z}{z-3}\, dz, \quad \Gamma_2 = \{z : |z-3| = \tfrac{1}{2}\}$

Section 2

Exercise 2.1 Evaluate each of the following integrals by using either Cauchy's Integral Formula or Cauchy's Theorem, as appropriate. In each case, $\Gamma = \{z : |z-1| = 2\}$.

(a) $\displaystyle\int_{\Gamma} \frac{e^{i\pi z/2}}{z-1}\, dz$
(b) $\displaystyle\int_{\Gamma} \frac{z^3}{z-2}\, dz$
(c) $\displaystyle\int_{\Gamma} \frac{z+4}{z-4}\, dz$

(d) $\displaystyle\int_{\Gamma} \frac{\sin z}{z-i}\, dz$
(e) $\displaystyle\int_{\Gamma} \frac{z^2}{z^2-4}\, dz$

Exercise 2.2 Use partial fractions and Cauchy's Integral Formula to evaluate the following integrals. In each case, $\Gamma = \{z : |z-1| = 3\}$.

(a) $\displaystyle\int_{\Gamma} \frac{2z}{z^2-1}\, dz$
(b) $\displaystyle\int_{\Gamma} \frac{\sin 2z}{z^2+1}\, dz$
(c) $\displaystyle\int_{\Gamma} \frac{6\cosh z}{z(z^2-9)}\, dz$

Exercise 2.3

(a) Use Liouville's Theorem to show that if f is an entire function such that

$$|f(z)| \geq K, \qquad \text{for all } z \in \mathbb{C},$$

for some $K > 0$, then f is a constant function.

(b) By finding a counter-example, show that the above result is not valid if the condition on $|f(z)|$ is replaced by

$$|f(z)| > 0, \qquad \text{for all } z \in \mathbb{C}.$$

Section 3

Exercise 3.1 Evaluate each of the following integrals by applying Cauchy's nth Derivative Formula. In each case, $\Gamma = \{z : |z| = 2\}$.

(a) $\displaystyle\int_{\Gamma} \frac{\cos z}{(z - \pi/2)^2}\, dz$
(b) $\displaystyle\int_{\Gamma} \frac{\cosh \pi z}{(z-i)^3}\, dz$
(c) $\displaystyle\int_{\Gamma} \frac{\sin z}{(z^2 + 2z - 3)^2}\, dz$

(d) $\displaystyle\int_{\Gamma} \frac{\sin 2z}{(z - \pi/4)^5}\, dz$
(e) $\displaystyle\int_{\Gamma} \frac{1}{(z+1)^{11}}\, dz$

Exercise 3.2 Evaluate

$$\int_{\Gamma} \frac{e^{3z}}{z^4 - 2z^3 + z^2}\, dz, \qquad \text{where } \Gamma = \{z : |z| = 3\}.$$

Exercise 3.3 Use the Analyticity of Derivatives to prove that there is no analytic function F such that

$$F'(z) = \mathrm{Re}\, z, \qquad \text{for all } z \text{ in } \mathbb{C}.$$

Section 4

Exercise 4.1 All but two of the following integrals can be evaluated by the methods *introduced* in this unit. Identify these two integrals and say how you would evaluate them. Evaluate the other seven integrals.

The contours Γ_1, Γ_2 and Γ_3 are as follows:

Γ_1 is the line segment from -1 to i;

Γ_2 is the triangular contour shown in the figure in the margin;

Γ_3 is the circle $\{z : |z| = 2\}$.

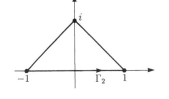

(a) $\displaystyle\int_{\Gamma_2} \sin z \, dz$ (b) $\displaystyle\int_{\Gamma_2} \sin(z^2) \, dz$ (c) $\displaystyle\int_{\Gamma_2} \frac{1}{z+i} \, dz$

(d) $\displaystyle\int_{\Gamma_1} z \sin z \, dz$ (e) $\displaystyle\int_{\Gamma_3} \frac{\sin z}{z^2} \, dz$ (f) $\displaystyle\int_{\Gamma_3} \frac{\cosh z}{z^5} \, dz$

(g) $\displaystyle\int_{\Gamma_3} \frac{z^5}{\cosh \frac{1}{2} z} \, dz$ (h) $\displaystyle\int_{\Gamma_2} \frac{z}{4z^2 + 1} \, dz$ (i) $\displaystyle\int_{\Gamma_3} \operatorname{Re} z \, dz$

Exercise 4.2 Evaluate

$$\int_\Gamma \frac{\exp(z^n)}{z} \, dz,$$

where Γ is the circle $\{z : |z| = 1\}$ and n is a positive integer.

Hence show that

$$\int_0^{2\pi} e^{\cos nt} \cos(\sin nt) \, dt = 2\pi.$$

Section 5

There are no exercises for Section 5.

SOLUTIONS TO THE PROBLEMS

Section 1

1.1 The regions in parts (a), (b), (d), (e), (g), (h) are simply-connected (because each one has no holes in it); the regions in parts (c), (f) are not simply-connected (because each has at least one hole in it, two in the case of (c) and one in the case of (f)).

1.2 **(a)** The points A, C and D lie on the inside of Γ.

(b) There are several possible algorithms. This one makes use of the fact that, since Γ is simple-closed, it lies in some closed disc $D = \{z : |z| \leq r\}$, say. Hence, any point in $\mathbb{C} - D$ lies in the outside of Γ.

Choose a point β in $\mathbb{C} - D$. From the given point α, draw a line segment from α to β, and count the number of times that the line crosses Γ (see the above figure). If this number is *odd*, then α lies inside Γ; if it is *even*, then α lies outside Γ.

1.3 **(a)** No, f is not analytic on $\mathcal{R}$.

(b) Yes, even though Γ is not simple-closed.

(c) No, f is not analytic on $\mathcal{R}$.

(d) Yes, even though f is not analytic at 3.

(e) No, Γ is not closed.

(f) No, f is not analytic on $\mathcal{R}$.

1.4 Let $\mathcal{R}$ be a simply-connected region which contains Γ, but excludes the point α. Then Γ is a closed contour in $\mathcal{R}$, and $f(z) = (z - \alpha)^{-1}$ is analytic on $\mathcal{R}$. Thus the conditions of Cauchy's Theorem are satisfied, and so

$$\int_\Gamma \frac{1}{z - \alpha}\, dz = 0.$$

1.5 Let $\Gamma = \Gamma_1 + \widetilde{\Gamma}_2$. Then Γ is a closed contour in $\mathcal{R}$, and it follows from Cauchy's Theorem that

$$\int_\Gamma f(z)\, dz = \int_{\Gamma_1} f(z)\, dz + \int_{\widetilde{\Gamma}_2} f(z)\, dz = 0.$$

But, by the Reverse Contour Theorem,

$$\int_{\widetilde{\Gamma}_2} f(z)\, dz = -\int_{\Gamma_2} f(z)\, dz.$$

Thus

$$\int_{\Gamma_1} f(z)\, dz = \int_{\Gamma_2} f(z)\, dz.$$

1.6 By the Shrinking Contour Theorem, we can replace Γ by any circle lying inside Γ; for example, the unit circle C. Thus

$$\int_\Gamma z^{-1}\, dz = \int_C z^{-1}\, dz = 2\pi i,$$

as we saw at the beginning of Subsection 1.1.

Section 2

2.1 **(a)** We use Cauchy's Integral Formula with $f(z) = \sin z$, $\alpha = -i$, and $\mathcal{R} = \mathbb{C}$. Then $\mathcal{R}$ is simply-connected, $\Gamma = \{z : |z| = 2\}$ is a simple-closed contour in $\mathcal{R}$, and α lies inside Γ. Also, f is analytic on $\mathcal{R}$.

It follows from the Integral Formula that

$$\begin{aligned}
\int_\Gamma \frac{\sin z}{z + i}\, dz &= 2\pi i\, f(-i) \\
&= 2\pi i \sin(-i) \\
&= 2\pi \sinh 1.
\end{aligned}$$

(b) We use Cauchy's Integral Formula with $f(z) = 3z$, $\alpha = -1$, and $\mathcal{R} = \mathbb{C}$. Then $\mathcal{R}$ is simply-connected, $\Gamma = \{z : |z - 3| = 5\}$ is a simple-closed contour in $\mathcal{R}$, and α lies inside Γ. Also, f is analytic on $\mathcal{R}$.

It follows from the Integral Formula that

$$\begin{aligned}
\int_\Gamma \frac{3z}{z + 1}\, dz &= 2\pi i f(-1) \\
&= -6\pi i.
\end{aligned}$$

2.2 **(a)** The integrand is not defined at the points 2 (inside Γ) and -2 (outside Γ).

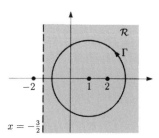

We therefore take $f(z) = e^{3z}/(z + 2)$ and $\alpha = 2$, and let $\mathcal{R}$ be any simply-connected region which contains Γ but not the point -2; for example, $\mathcal{R} = \{z : \operatorname{Re} z > -\frac{3}{2}\}$. Then Γ is a simple-closed contour in $\mathcal{R}$, and α lies inside Γ. Also, f is analytic on $\mathcal{R}$.

It follows from Cauchy's Integral Formula that

$$\begin{aligned}
\int_\Gamma \frac{e^{3z}}{z^2 - 4}\, dz &= \int_\Gamma \frac{f(z)}{z - 2}\, dz \\
&= 2\pi i\, f(2) \\
&= 2\pi i \cdot \left(\frac{e^6}{4}\right) = \tfrac{1}{2}\pi e^6 i.
\end{aligned}$$

(b) The integrand is not defined at the points 0 (inside Γ) and $2i$ and $-2i$ (both outside Γ).

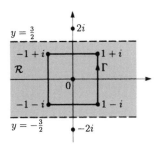

We therefore take $f(z) = (\cos 2z)/(z^2 + 4)$ and $\alpha = 0$, and let $\mathcal{R}$ be any simply-connected region which contains Γ but not the points $2i$ and $-2i$; for example, $\mathcal{R} = \left\{ z : -\frac{3}{2} < \operatorname{Im} z < \frac{3}{2} \right\}$. Then Γ is a simple-closed contour in $\mathcal{R}$, and α lies inside Γ. Also, f is analytic on $\mathcal{R}$.

It follows from Cauchy's Integral Formula that
$$\int_\Gamma \frac{\cos 2z}{z(z^2 + 4)}\, dz = \int_\Gamma \frac{f(z)}{z - 0}\, dz$$
$$= 2\pi i\, f(0)$$
$$= 2\pi i \cdot \frac{\cos 0}{(0^2 + 4)} = \tfrac{1}{2}\pi i.$$

2.3 (a) Let $\dfrac{1}{z^2 - z} = \dfrac{1}{z(z - 1)} = \dfrac{A}{z} + \dfrac{B}{z - 1}$.

Multiplying both sides by $z^2 - z$, we obtain
$$1 = A(z - 1) + Bz. \tag{$*$}$$
Comparing the coefficients of z and constants, we obtain
$$z: \quad 0 = A + B$$
$$1: \quad 1 = -A.$$
Solving these simultaneous equations gives $A = -1$, $B = 1$. Thus
$$\frac{1}{z^2 - z} = -\frac{1}{z} + \frac{1}{z - 1}.$$
(*Alternatively*, putting $z = 0$ in $(*)$ gives $A = -1$, and putting $z = 1$ gives $B = 1$.)

(b) Let $\dfrac{1}{z(z - 2)} = \dfrac{A}{z} + \dfrac{B}{z - 2}$.

Multiplying both sides by $z(z - 2)$, we get
$$1 = A(z - 2) + Bz.$$
Comparing the coefficients of z and constants, we obtain
$$z: \quad 0 = A + B$$
$$1: \quad 1 = -2A.$$
Solving these simultaneous equations gives $A = -\frac{1}{2}$, $B = \frac{1}{2}$. Thus
$$\frac{1}{z(z - 2)} = -\frac{1}{2z} + \frac{1}{2(z - 2)}.$$

2.4 First note that
$$z^2 - z = z(z - 1),$$
and both 0 and 1 lie inside Γ.

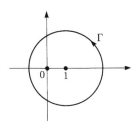

Using partial fractions, we can write
$$\frac{1}{z^2 - z} = -\frac{1}{z} + \frac{1}{z - 1}, \quad \text{by Problem 2.3(a)},$$
and so
$$\int_\Gamma \frac{\cos 3z}{z^2 - z}\, dz = -\int_\Gamma \frac{\cos 3z}{z}\, dz + \int_\Gamma \frac{\cos 3z}{z - 1}\, dz.$$
We now use Cauchy's Integral Formula with $f(z) = \cos 3z$, $\mathcal{R} = \mathbb{C}$, and $\alpha = 0$ and 1 (in turn). Then $\mathcal{R}$ is simply-connected, Γ is a simple-closed contour in $\mathcal{R}$, and f is analytic on $\mathcal{R}$. We obtain
$$\int_\Gamma \frac{\cos 3z}{z}\, dz = 2\pi i\, f(0) = 2\pi i,$$
and $\quad \displaystyle\int_\Gamma \frac{\cos 3z}{z - 1}\, dz = 2\pi i\, f(1) = 2\pi i \cos 3.$

Thus
$$\int_\Gamma \frac{\cos 3z}{z^2 - z}\, dz = -2\pi i + 2\pi i \cos 3$$
$$= 2\pi i\, (\cos 3 - 1).$$

2.5 (a) We have
$$\int_\Gamma \frac{e^z}{z^4 - 1}\, dz = \frac{1}{4} \int_\Gamma \frac{e^z}{z - 1}\, dz - \frac{1}{4} \int_\Gamma \frac{e^z}{z + 1}\, dz$$
$$+ \frac{i}{4} \int_\Gamma \frac{e^z}{z - i}\, dz - \frac{i}{4} \int_\Gamma \frac{e^z}{z + i}\, dz.$$

(i) All four points 1, -1, i, $-i$ lie inside Γ. We use Cauchy's Integral Formula with $f(z) = e^z$, $\mathcal{R} = \mathbb{C}$, and $\alpha = 1$, -1, i and $-i$ (in turn).

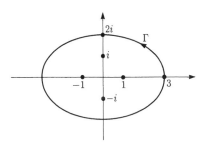

Then $\mathcal{R}$ is simply-connected, Γ is a simple-closed contour in $\mathcal{R}$, and f is analytic on $\mathcal{R}$. Thus
$$\int_\Gamma \frac{e^z}{z - 1}\, dz = 2\pi i\, f(1) = 2\pi i e;$$
$$\int_\Gamma \frac{e^z}{z + 1}\, dz = 2\pi i\, f(-1) = 2\pi i e^{-1};$$
$$\int_\Gamma \frac{e^z}{z - i}\, dz = 2\pi i\, f(i) = 2\pi i e^{i};$$
$$\int_\Gamma \frac{e^z}{z + i}\, dz = 2\pi i\, f(-i) = 2\pi i e^{-i}.$$
Putting all this together, we obtain
$$\int_\Gamma \frac{e^z}{z^4 - 1}\, dz = \tfrac{1}{4}(2\pi i\, (e - e^{-1} + ie^{i} - ie^{-i}))$$
$$= \pi i\, (\sinh 1 - \sin 1).$$

(ii) In this part, only the two points i and $-i$ lie inside Γ. The value of the integral is therefore

$$\tfrac{1}{4}\left(2\pi i\left(ie^i - ie^{-i}\right)\right) = -\pi i \sin 1.$$

(The other two terms are each 0, by Cauchy's Theorem.)

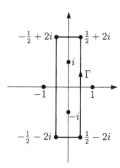

(b) First note that

$$z^4 - 1 = (z^2 - 1)(z^2 + 1)$$
$$= (z-1)(z+1)(z-i)(z+i)$$

and that i and $-i$ lie inside Γ, but 1 and -1 lie outside Γ. Also

$$\frac{1}{z^2 + 1} = \frac{-i/2}{z - i} + \frac{i/2}{z + i} \quad \text{(by Example 2.3),}$$

and so

$$\int_\Gamma \frac{e^z}{z^4 - 1}\, dz = -\frac{i}{2}\int_\Gamma \frac{e^z/(z^2 - 1)}{z - i}\, dz$$
$$+ \frac{i}{2}\int_\Gamma \frac{e^z/(z^2 - 1)}{z + i}\, dz.$$

We now let $\mathcal{R}$ be any simply-connected region containing Γ, but not the points 1 and -1; for example, $\mathcal{R} = \{z : -\frac{3}{4} < \operatorname{Re} z < \frac{3}{4}\}$. Applying Cauchy's Integral Formula with $f(z) = e^z/(z^2 - 1)$, which is analytic on $\mathcal{R}$, and $\alpha = i$ and $-i$ (in turn) gives

$$\int_\Gamma \frac{e^z}{z^4 - 1}\, dz = -\frac{i}{2}2\pi i f(i) + \frac{i}{2}2\pi i f(-i)$$
$$= \pi\left(\frac{e^i}{-2} - \frac{e^{-i}}{-2}\right)$$
$$= -\pi i \sin 1, \text{ as before.}$$

2.6 We used the fact that f is analytic on $\mathcal{R}$ in Step (a), when we applied the Shrinking Contour Theorem, which is valid for analytic functions. Also, in Step (c) we used the fact that f is differentiable at α to deduce that f is continuous at α.

2.7 We apply Cauchy's Integral Formula with $\Gamma = C$ and α the centre of C. Then

$$f(\alpha) = \frac{1}{2\pi i}\int_C \frac{f(z)}{z - \alpha}\, dz.$$

The standard parametrization for C is

$$\gamma(t) = \alpha + re^{it} \quad (t \in [0, 2\pi]);$$

so

$$f(\alpha) = \frac{1}{2\pi i}\int_0^{2\pi} \frac{1}{re^{it}} f(\alpha + re^{it})rie^{it}dt$$
$$= \frac{1}{2\pi}\int_0^{2\pi} f(\alpha + re^{it})\, dt.$$

2.8 It is not true that $|\sin z| \le 1$ for all $z \in \mathbb{C}$; for example,

$$|\sin i| = \left|\frac{e^{i^2} - e^{-i^2}}{2i}\right| = 1.175 \text{ (to 3 decimal places).}$$

2.9 We use the method of proof by contradiction. Assume that the function

$$f(z) = \exp(i|z|)$$

is an entire function. Now, for $z \in \mathbb{C}$,

$$|f(z)| = \left|\exp(i|z|)\right|$$
$$= \left|\cos|z| + i\sin|z|\right|, \text{ by definition,}$$
$$= 1,$$

so f is bounded. Hence, by Liouville's Theorem, f is a constant function. But, for example,

$$f(0) = \exp 0 = 1,$$

and $\quad f(1) = \exp i = \cos 1 + i\sin 1.$

Thus $f(0) \ne f(1)$, and so we have a contradiction. It follows that f is not an entire function.

Section 3

3.1 (a) We use Cauchy's First Derivative Formula with $f(z) = e^{2z}$, $\alpha = -1$ and $\mathcal{R} = \mathbb{C}$. Then $\mathcal{R}$ is simply-connected, $\Gamma = \{z : |z| = 3\}$ is a simple-closed contour in $\mathcal{R}$, and α lies inside Γ. Also, f is analytic on $\mathcal{R}$. It follows from the First Derivative Formula that

$$\int_\Gamma \frac{e^{2z}}{(z+1)^2}\, dz = 2\pi i\, f'(-1).$$

But $f'(z) = 2e^{2z}$, so $f'(-1) = 2e^{-2}$. Thus

$$\int_\Gamma \frac{e^{2z}}{(z+1)^2}\, dz = 4\pi e^{-2}i.$$

(b) The integrand is not analytic at 0 and -1, both of which lie inside $\Gamma = \{z : |z| = 3\}$. Thus, we must first express $1/(z(z+1)^2)$ in partial fractions. We write

$$\frac{1}{z(z+1)^2} = \frac{A}{z} + \frac{B}{z+1} + \frac{C}{(z+1)^2}.$$

Multiplying both sides by $z(z+1)^2$, we obtain

$$1 = A(z+1)^2 + Bz(z+1) + Cz.$$

Comparing the coefficients of z^2, z and constants, we obtain

$$z^2: \quad 0 = A + B$$
$$z: \quad 0 = 2A + B + C$$
$$1: \quad 1 = A.$$

So $A = 1$, $B = -1$, $C = -1$. Thus

$$\frac{1}{z(z+1)^2} = \frac{1}{z} - \frac{1}{z+1} - \frac{1}{(z+1)^2},$$

and hence

$$\int_\Gamma \frac{e^{2z}}{z(z+1)^2}\, dz$$
$$= \int_\Gamma \frac{e^{2z}}{z}\, dz - \int_\Gamma \frac{e^{2z}}{z+1}\, dz - \int_\Gamma \frac{e^{2z}}{(z+1)^2}\, dz.$$

We now use Cauchy's Integral Formula and the First Derivative Formula with $f(z) = e^{2z}$, $\alpha = 0$ and -1, and $\mathcal{R} = \mathbb{C}$. Then $\mathcal{R}$ is simply-connected, Γ is a simple-closed contour in $\mathcal{R}$, and α lies inside Γ (for each value of α). Also, f is analytic on $\mathcal{R}$.

It follows from Cauchy's Integral Formula that
$$\int_\Gamma \frac{e^{2z}}{z}\, dz = 2\pi i\, f(0) = 2\pi i e^0 = 2\pi i$$
and
$$\int_\Gamma \frac{e^{2z}}{z+1}\, dz = 2\pi i\, f(-1) = 2\pi e^{-2} i,$$
and from the First Derivative Formula that
$$\int_\Gamma \frac{e^{2z}}{(z+1)^2}\, dz = 2\pi i\, f'(-1)$$
$$= 2\pi i \cdot 2e^{-2} = 4\pi e^{-2} i.$$
Putting all this together, we obtain
$$\int_\Gamma \frac{e^{2z}}{z(z+1)^2}\, dz = 2\pi i \left(1 - e^{-2} - 2e^{-2}\right)$$
$$= 2\pi i \left(1 - 3e^{-2}\right).$$

3.2 **(a)** We use Cauchy's nth Derivative Formula with $n = 2$, $f(z) = \cosh 2z$, $\alpha = -i$, and $\mathcal{R} = \mathbb{C}$.

Then $\mathcal{R}$ is simply-connected, $\Gamma = \{z : |z| = 2\}$ is a simple-closed contour in $\mathcal{R}$, and α lies inside Γ. Also, f is analytic on $\mathcal{R}$.

It follows from the nth Derivative Formula that
$$\int_\Gamma \frac{\cosh 2z}{(z+i)^3}\, dz = 2\pi i \frac{f''(-i)}{2!}.$$
But $f''(z) = 4\cosh 2z$, so
$$f''(-i) = 4\cosh(-2i) = 4\cos 2.$$
Thus
$$\int_\Gamma \frac{\cosh 2z}{(z+i)^3}\, dz = 4\pi i \cos 2.$$

(b) We use Cauchy's nth Derivative Formula with $n = 9$, $f(z) = ze^z$, $\alpha = 1$, and $\mathcal{R} = \mathbb{C}$. Then $\mathcal{R}$ is simply-connected, $\Gamma = \{z : |z| = 2\}$ is a simple-closed contour in $\mathcal{R}$, and α lies inside Γ. Also, f is analytic on $\mathcal{R}$.

It follows from the nth Derivative Formula that
$$\int_\Gamma \frac{ze^z}{(z-1)^{10}}\, dz = 2\pi i \frac{f^{(9)}(1)}{9!}.$$
But $f'(z) = e^z + ze^z$, $f''(z) = 2e^z + ze^z, \ldots,$
$f^{(9)}(z) = 9e^z + ze^z$; so
$$f^{(9)}(1) = 10e.$$
Thus
$$\int_\Gamma \frac{ze^z}{(z-1)^{10}}\, dz = \frac{20e\pi i}{9!} = \frac{e\pi i}{18144}.$$

(c) The integrand is not analytic at 0 and -1, both of which lie inside Γ. Thus, we must first express $1/(z^3(z+1))$ in partial fractions. We write
$$\frac{1}{z^3(z+1)} = \frac{A}{z} + \frac{B}{z^2} + \frac{C}{z^3} + \frac{D}{z+1}.$$
Multiplying both sides by $z^3(z+1)$, we obtain
$$1 = Az^2(z+1) + Bz(z+1) + C(z+1) + Dz^3.$$
Comparing the coefficients of z^3, z^2, z and constants, we obtain
$$z^3: \quad 0 = A + D$$
$$z^2: \quad 0 = A + B$$
$$z: \quad 0 = B + C$$
$$1: \quad 1 = C.$$

So $A = C = 1$, $B = D = -1$, and
$$\frac{1}{z^3(z+1)} = \frac{1}{z} - \frac{1}{z^2} + \frac{1}{z^3} - \frac{1}{z+1}.$$
Thus
$$\int_\Gamma \frac{e^{2z}}{z^3(z+1)}\, dz$$
$$= \int_\Gamma \frac{e^{2z}}{z}\, dz - \int_\Gamma \frac{e^{2z}}{z^2}\, dz + \int_\Gamma \frac{e^{2z}}{z^3}\, dz - \int_\Gamma \frac{e^{2z}}{z+1}\, dz.$$
We now use Cauchy's Integral Formula and the First and Second Derivative Formulas with $f(z) = e^{2z}$, $\alpha = 0$ and -1, and $\mathcal{R} = \mathbb{C}$. Then $\mathcal{R}$ is simply-connected, $\Gamma = \{z : |z| = 2\}$ is a simple-closed contour in $\mathcal{R}$, and α lies inside Γ (for each value of α). Also, f is analytic on $\mathcal{R}$.

It follows from Cauchy's Integral Formula that
$$\int_\Gamma \frac{e^{2z}}{z}\, dz = 2\pi i\, f(0) = 2\pi i,$$
and
$$\int_\Gamma \frac{e^{2z}}{z+1}\, dz = 2\pi i\, f(-1) = 2\pi e^{-2} i,$$
and from the First Derivative Formula that
$$\int_\Gamma \frac{e^{2z}}{z^2}\, dz = 2\pi i\, f'(0)$$
$$= 2\pi i \cdot 2e^0 = 4\pi i,$$
and from the Second Derivative Formula that
$$\int_\Gamma \frac{e^{2z}}{z^3}\, dz = 2\pi i \frac{f''(0)}{2!}$$
$$= 2\pi i \cdot 4e^0/2! = 4\pi i.$$
Thus
$$\int_\Gamma \frac{e^{2z}}{z^3(z+1)}\, dz = 2\pi i - 2\pi e^{-2} i - 4\pi i + 4\pi i$$
$$= 2\pi i(1 - e^{-2}).$$

3.3 By Cauchy's nth Derivative Formula, with $\Gamma = \{z : |z - \alpha| = r\}$,
$$f^{(n)}(\alpha) = \frac{n!}{2\pi i} \int_\Gamma \frac{f(z)}{(z-\alpha)^{n+1}}\, dz.$$
On Γ, $|z - \alpha| = r$ and $|f(z)| \leq K$.

Hence, by the Estimation Theorem, with $M = K/r^{n+1}$ and $L = 2\pi r$, we have
$$|f^{(n)}(\alpha)| \leq \frac{n!}{2\pi} \cdot \frac{K}{r^{n+1}} \cdot 2\pi r$$
$$= \frac{Kn!}{r^n}.$$

3.4 **(a)** Assume that there exists an analytic function F such that $F'(z) = |z|$, $z \in \mathbb{C}$. Then, by the Analyticity of Derivatives, F' is analytic on $\mathbb{C}$. But $F'(z) = |z|$, which is not analytic on $\mathbb{C}$. This contradiction implies that no such function F exists.

(b) Since f is entire, so is f', by the Analyticity of Derivatives. Since f' is entire and bounded, f' is constant, by Liouville's Theorem.

Let $f'(z) = \alpha$, where $\alpha \in \mathbb{C}$. Then the function $z \longmapsto \alpha z$ is a primitive of f' on $\mathbb{C}$, so
$$f(z) = \alpha z + \beta, \qquad \text{where } \alpha, \beta \in \mathbb{C}$$
(see *Unit B1*, Problem 3.6).

Section 4

4.1 (a) Let $\dfrac{1}{z(z-3)} = \dfrac{A}{z-3} + \dfrac{B}{z}$.

Multiplying both sides by $z(z-3)$, we obtain

$1 = Az + B(z-3)$.

Comparing the coefficients of z and constants, we obtain

$z:\quad 0 = A + B$

$1:\quad 1 = -3B$.

These simultaneous equations have the solutions

$A = \tfrac{1}{3}, \quad B = -\tfrac{1}{3}$.

Thus

$\dfrac{1}{z(z-3)} = \dfrac{1/3}{z-3} - \dfrac{1/3}{z}$.

(b) Let $\dfrac{1}{z^2(z-3)} = \dfrac{A}{z-3} + \dfrac{B}{z} + \dfrac{C}{z^2}$.

Multiplying both sides by $z^2(z-3)$, we obtain

$1 = Az^2 + Bz(z-3) + C(z-3)$.

Comparing the coefficients of z^2, z and constants, we obtain

$z^2:\quad 0 = A + B$

$z:\quad 0 = -3B + C$

$1:\quad 1 = -3C$.

These simultaneous equations have the solutions

$A = \tfrac{1}{9}, \quad B = -\tfrac{1}{9}, \quad C = -\tfrac{1}{3}$.

Thus

$\dfrac{1}{z^2(z-3)} = \dfrac{1/9}{z-3} - \dfrac{1/9}{z} - \dfrac{1/3}{z^2}$.

(c) Let $\dfrac{1}{z^3(z-3)} = \dfrac{A}{z-3} + \dfrac{B}{z} + \dfrac{C}{z^2} + \dfrac{D}{z^3}$.

Multiplying both sides by $z^3(z-3)$, we obtain

$1 = Az^3 + Bz^2(z-3) + Cz(z-3) + D(z-3)$.

Comparing the coefficients of z^3, z^2, z and constants, we obtain

$z^3:\quad 0 = A + B$

$z^2:\quad 0 = -3B + C$

$z:\quad 0 = -3C + D$

$1:\quad 1 = -3D$.

These simultaneous equations have the solutions

$A = \tfrac{1}{27}, \quad B = -\tfrac{1}{27}, \quad C = -\tfrac{1}{9}, \quad D = -\tfrac{1}{3}$.

Thus

$\dfrac{1}{z^3(z-3)} = \dfrac{1/27}{z-3} - \dfrac{1/27}{z} - \dfrac{1/9}{z^2} - \dfrac{1/3}{z^3}$.

4.2 (a) Using the boxed result in Frame 3 (a special case of Cauchy's Integral Formula), we have

$\displaystyle\int_\Gamma \frac{1}{z}\,dz = 2\pi i,$

since 0 lies inside $\Gamma = \{z : |z-1| = 2\}$.

(The integral *can* also be evaluated by using the standard parametrization for the circle Γ.)

(b) Using the boxed result in Frame 2 (a special case of Cauchy's Theorem), we have

$\displaystyle\int_\Gamma \frac{1}{z-5}\,dz = 0,$

since 5 lies outside $\Gamma = \{z : |z-1| = 2\}$.

(The integral can also be evaluated by using the standard parametrization for the circle Γ.)

(c) The standard parametrization for $\Gamma = \{z : |z-1| = 2\}$ is

$\gamma(t) = 1 + 2e^{it} \quad (t \in [0, 2\pi])$.

Hence

$\displaystyle\int_\Gamma \frac{1}{(z-1)^2}\,dz = \int_0^{2\pi} \frac{1}{(2e^{it})^2}\cdot 2ie^{it}\,dt$

$\displaystyle\qquad = \frac{i}{2}\int_0^{2\pi} e^{-it}\,dt$

$\displaystyle\qquad = \frac{i}{2}\left(\int_0^{2\pi}\cos t\,dt - i\int_0^{2\pi}\sin t\,dt\right) = 0.$

This integral can also be evaluated by using Cauchy's First Derivative Formula, with $f(z) = 1$, $\alpha = 1$, and $\mathcal{R} = \mathbb{C}$. Then α lies inside $\Gamma = \{z : |z-1| = 2\}$, which is a simple-closed contour in $\mathcal{R}$. Also, f is analytic on $\mathcal{R}$. By the First Derivative Formula,

$\displaystyle\int_\Gamma \frac{1}{(z-1)^2}\,dz = \frac{1}{2\pi i}f'(1) = 0.$

4.3 The integrand $z \longmapsto \dfrac{e^z}{z^3(z^2-9)}$ is analytic except at 0, 3 (inside $\Gamma = \{z : |z-2| = 3\}$) and -3 (outside Γ). Hence we choose

$f(z) = \dfrac{e^z}{z+3},$

which is analytic on $\mathcal{R} = \{z : \operatorname{Re} z > -2\}$, as in Frames 5 and 6. As noted there, $\mathcal{R}$ is simply-connected and $\Gamma \subseteq \mathcal{R}$. Thus

$\displaystyle\int_\Gamma \frac{e^z}{z^3(z^2-9)}\,dz = \int_\Gamma \frac{f(z)}{z^3(z-3)}\,dz.$

We now express $1/(z^3(z-3))$ in partial fractions. By Problem 4.1(c), we have

$\dfrac{1}{z^3(z-3)} = \dfrac{1/27}{z-3} - \dfrac{1/27}{z} - \dfrac{1/9}{z^2} - \dfrac{1/3}{z^3},$

and so

$\displaystyle\int_\Gamma \frac{f(z)}{z^3(z-3)}\,dz = \frac{1}{27}\int_\Gamma \frac{f(z)}{z-3}\,dz - \frac{1}{27}\int_\Gamma \frac{f(z)}{z}\,dz$

$\displaystyle\qquad\qquad - \frac{1}{9}\int_\Gamma \frac{f(z)}{z^2}\,dz - \frac{1}{3}\int_\Gamma \frac{f(z)}{z^3}\,dz.$

Applying Cauchy's Integral Formula to the first and second integrals on the right-hand side, and Cauchy's First Derivative Formula to the third and Cauchy's Second Derivative Formula to the fourth, gives

$\displaystyle\int_\Gamma \frac{f(z)}{z^3(z-3)}\,dz = \frac{1}{27}2\pi i f(3) - \frac{1}{27}2\pi i f(0)$

$\displaystyle\qquad\qquad - \frac{1}{9}2\pi i f'(0) - \frac{1}{3}\cdot\frac{2\pi i}{2!}f''(0)$

$\displaystyle\qquad = \frac{1}{27}2\pi i\left(\frac{e^3}{6}\right) - \frac{1}{27}2\pi i\left(\frac{1}{3}\right)$

$\displaystyle\qquad\qquad - \frac{1}{9}2\pi i\left(\frac{2}{9}\right) - \frac{1}{3}\pi i\left(\frac{5}{27}\right),$

since

$f'(z) = (z+2)e^z/(z+3)^2$

and

$f''(z) = (z^2 + 4z + 5)e^z/(z+3)^3.$

Simplifying this, we obtain

$\displaystyle\int_\Gamma \frac{f(z)}{z^3(z-3)}\,dz = \frac{\pi i}{81}(e^3 - 11).$

4.4 (a) In this case,
$$g(z) = e^{2z} \quad \text{and} \quad p(z) = z(z^2 + 1).$$
The three steps of the strategy are as follows.
Step (a) $\quad p(z) = q(z)r(z),$
where
$$q(z) = (z - i)z \quad \text{and} \quad r(z) = z + i.$$
The zeros, i and 0, of q lie inside $\Gamma = \left\{ z : |z - i/2| = \frac{3}{4} \right\}$ and the zero of r lies outside Γ, as shown in the figure.

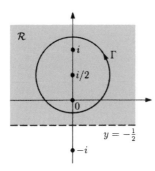

Then $f(z) = g(z)/r(z) = e^{2z}/(z + i)$ is analytic on, for example, $\mathcal{R} = \left\{ z : \operatorname{Im} z > -\frac{1}{2} \right\}$, which contains Γ.

Step (b) $\quad$ Let $\dfrac{1}{q(z)} = \dfrac{1}{(z - i)z} = \dfrac{A}{z - i} + \dfrac{B}{z}.$

Multiplying both sides by $(z - i)z$, we obtain
$$1 = Az + B(z - i).$$
Comparing the coefficients of z and constants, we obtain
$$z : \quad 0 = A + B$$
$$1 : \quad 1 = -Bi.$$
Solving these simultaneous equations gives $A = -i$, $B = i$.

Thus
$$\frac{1}{q(z)} = -\frac{i}{z - i} + \frac{i}{z}.$$

Step (c) $\quad \displaystyle\int_\Gamma \frac{e^{2z}}{z(z^2 + 1)}\, dz = -i \int_\Gamma \frac{e^{2z}/(z + i)}{z - i}\, dz$
$$+ i \int_\Gamma \frac{e^{2z}/(z + i)}{z}\, dz.$$

Applying Cauchy's Integral Formula to each of the integrals on the right-hand side, we obtain
$$\int_\Gamma \frac{e^{2z}}{z(z^2 + 1)}\, dz = -i(2\pi i f(i)) + i(2\pi i f(0))$$
$$= 2\pi(e^{2i}/(2i) - 1/i)$$
$$= 2\pi(i - \tfrac{1}{2}i(\cos 2 + i \sin 2))$$
$$= \pi \sin 2 + (2 - \cos 2)\pi i.$$

(b) In this case,
$$g(z) = e^{2z} \quad \text{and} \quad p(z) = z^2(z^2 + 1).$$
Step (a) $\quad p(z) = q(z)r(z),$
where
$$q(z) = (z - i)z^2 \quad \text{and} \quad r(z) = z + i.$$
The zeros, i and 0, of q lie inside $\Gamma = \left\{ z : |z - i/2| = \frac{3}{4} \right\}$ and the zero of r lies outside Γ.

Then $f(z) = g(z)/r(z) = e^{2z}/(z + i)$ is analytic on, for example, $\mathcal{R} = \left\{ z : \operatorname{Im} z > -\frac{1}{2} \right\}$, which contains Γ.

Step (b) $\quad$ As you can check,
$$\frac{1}{q(z)} = -\frac{1}{z - i} + \frac{1}{z} + \frac{i}{z^2}.$$

Step (c) $\displaystyle\int_\Gamma \frac{e^{2z}}{z^2(z^2 + 1)}\, dz = -\int_\Gamma \frac{e^{2z}/(z + i)}{z - i}\, dz$
$$+ \int_\Gamma \frac{e^{2z}/(z + i)}{z}\, dz$$
$$+ i \int_\Gamma \frac{e^{2z}/(z + i)}{z^2}\, dz.$$

Applying Cauchy's Integral Formula to the first two integrals on the right-hand side, and applying Cauchy's First Derivative Formula to the third, we obtain
$$\int_\Gamma \frac{e^{2z}}{z^2(z^2 + 1)}\, dz = -2\pi i f(i) + 2\pi i f(0) + i \cdot 2\pi i f'(0)$$
$$= -2\pi i \frac{e^{2i}}{2i} + 2\pi i \frac{1}{i} + i \cdot 2\pi i(1 - 2i)$$
$$\text{since } f'(z) = (2z + 2i - 1)e^{2z}/(z + i)^2$$
$$= -\pi \cos 2 + (4 - \sin 2)\pi i.$$

4.5 From Frame 3,
$$\int_\Gamma \frac{1}{z - \frac{1}{2}}\, dz = 2\pi i, \tag{1}$$
where $\Gamma = \{ z : |z| = 1 \}$.
Using the standard parametrization for Γ,
$$\gamma(t) = e^{it} \quad (t \in [0, 2\pi]),$$
we obtain
$$\int_\Gamma \frac{1}{z - \frac{1}{2}}\, dz$$
$$= \int_0^{2\pi} \frac{1}{e^{it} - \frac{1}{2}} i e^{it}\, dt$$
$$= \int_0^{2\pi} \frac{e^{-it} - \frac{1}{2}}{(e^{it} - \frac{1}{2})(e^{-it} - \frac{1}{2})} i e^{it}\, dt$$
$$= \int_0^{2\pi} \frac{i - \frac{1}{2} i e^{it}}{\frac{5}{4} - \frac{1}{2}(e^{it} + e^{-it})}\, dt$$
$$= \int_0^{2\pi} \frac{\frac{1}{2} \sin t}{\frac{5}{4} - \cos t}\, dt + i \int_0^{2\pi} \frac{1 - \frac{1}{2}\cos t}{\frac{5}{4} - \cos t}\, dt. \tag{2}$$
Comparing (1) and (2), we deduce that
$$\int_0^{2\pi} \frac{2 \sin t}{5 - 4\cos t}\, dt = 0$$
and
$$\int_0^{2\pi} \frac{4 - 2\cos t}{5 - 4\cos t}\, dt = 2\pi.$$

Section 5

There are no problems in Section 5.

SOLUTIONS TO THE EXERCISES

Section 1

1.1 **(a)** The region $\{z : 2 < |z - 3| < 4\}$ is an annulus and so has a hole; therefore it is not simply-connected.

(b) The region $\{z : |z| > 0\}$ is a punctured plane and so has a hole (at 0); therefore it is not simply-connected.

(c) The region $\{z : -1 < \operatorname{Re} z < 1\}$ is a vertical strip and has no holes; therefore it is simply-connected.

(d) The region $\{z : -\pi < \operatorname{Arg} z < \pi\}$ is a cut-plane and so has no holes; therefore it is simply-connected.

(e) The domain of the tangent function is the region
$$\mathbb{C} - \{(n + \tfrac{1}{2})\pi : n \in \mathbb{Z}\},$$
which has holes at each of the points $(n + \tfrac{1}{2})\pi$, $n \in \mathbb{Z}$; therefore it is not simply-connected.

1.2 **(a)** The path $\Gamma : \gamma(t) = e^{it}$ $(t \in [0, \pi])$ is the upper half of the circle $\{z : |z| = 1\}$, with end-points $\gamma(0) = 1$ and $\gamma(\pi) = -1$. Thus Γ is not closed and hence not simple-closed.

(b) The path $\Gamma : \gamma(t) = e^{it}$ $(t \in [0, 2\pi])$ is the circle $\{z : |z| = 1\}$ traversed once. Hence Γ is simple-closed.

(c) The path $\Gamma : \gamma(t) = e^{it}$ $(t \in [0, 4\pi])$ is the circle $\{z : |z| = 1\}$ traversed twice (in the anticlockwise direction). Thus γ is not one-one on the interval $[0, 4\pi[$ (in particular, $\gamma(\pi) = \gamma(3\pi) = -1$) and hence Γ is not simple-closed.

(d) The path $\Gamma : \gamma(t) = te^{it}$ $(t \in [0, 2\pi])$ is not simple-closed because it is not closed ($\gamma(0) = 0$, but $\gamma(2\pi) = 2\pi$).

1.3 In each case the integrand is analytic on the simply-connected region $\mathcal{R}$ specified below, and each $\mathcal{R}$ contains the closed contour $\Gamma = \{z : |z| = 2\}$. Hence, by Cauchy's Theorem, the value of each integral is zero.

(a) $\mathcal{R} = \mathbb{C}$

(b) $\mathcal{R} = \{z : |z| < \pi\}$

(c) $\mathcal{R} = \{z : \operatorname{Re} z < 3\}$

(d) $\mathcal{R} = \{z : \operatorname{Im} z > -3\}$

(Other choices for $\mathcal{R}$ are possible.)

1.4 **(a)** The function sec is not defined at $\pi/2$, which lies inside $\Gamma = \{z : |z| = 2\}$.

(b) The function $z \longmapsto \operatorname{Log}(1 + z)$ is not analytic at -1, which lies on $\Gamma = \{z : |z| = 1\}$.

(c) The function $z \longmapsto 1/(z - 1)$ is not analytic at 1, which lies inside $\Gamma = \{z : |z| = 3\}$.

(d) The path $\Gamma : \gamma(t) = (1 - t) + it$ $(t \in [0, 1])$ is the line segment from 1 to i and so is not a closed contour.

1.5 **(a)** Let $\mathcal{R} = \mathbb{C}$. Then $\mathcal{R}$ is a simply-connected region on which $f(z) = ze^z$ is analytic. Also Γ_1 is the line segment from 0 to i and Γ_2 is the semi-circle with centre at $\tfrac{1}{2}i$ from 0 to i. Thus Γ_1 and Γ_2 are contours in $\mathcal{R}$ with the same initial and final points. Hence, by the Contour Independence Theorem,
$$\int_{\Gamma_1} ze^z \, dz = \int_{\Gamma_2} ze^z \, dz.$$

(b) Let $\mathcal{R} = \{z : \operatorname{Re} z > 0\}$. Then $\mathcal{R}$ is simply-connected and $g(z) = (\operatorname{Log} z)/(z - 3)$ is analytic on $\mathcal{R} - \{3\}$. Also $\Gamma_1 = \{z : |z - 4| = 2\}$ is a simple-closed contour (the circle with centre at 4 and radius 2) in $\mathcal{R}$ and Γ_2 (the circle with centre at 3 and radius $\tfrac{1}{2}$) lies inside Γ_1. Hence, by the Shrinking Contour Theorem,
$$\int_{\Gamma_1} \frac{\operatorname{Log} z}{z - 3} \, dz = \int_{\Gamma_2} \frac{\operatorname{Log} z}{z - 3} \, dz.$$

Section 2

2.1 Cauchy's Integral Formula is appropriate for all parts except part (c), in which we apply Cauchy's Theorem. The figure shows $\Gamma = \{z : |z - 1| = 2\}$ and points relevant to parts (a), (b), (d) and (e).

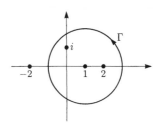

(a) Let $\mathcal{R} = \mathbb{C}$, which is simply-connected. Then $f(z) = e^{i\pi z/2}$ is analytic on $\mathcal{R}$, $\Gamma = \{z : |z - 1| = 2\}$ is a simple-closed contour in $\mathcal{R}$ and the point 1 lies inside Γ. Hence, by Cauchy's Integral Formula,
$$\int_\Gamma \frac{e^{i\pi z/2}}{z - 1} \, dz = 2\pi i f(1)$$
$$= 2\pi i e^{i\pi/2} = -2\pi.$$

(b) Let $\mathcal{R} = \mathbb{C}$, which is simply-connected. Then $f(z) = z^3$ is analytic on $\mathcal{R}$, $\Gamma = \{z : |z - 1| = 2\}$ is a simple-closed contour in $\mathcal{R}$ and the point 2 lies inside Γ. Hence, by Cauchy's Integral Formula,
$$\int_\Gamma \frac{z^3}{z - 2} \, dz = 2\pi i f(2)$$
$$= 2\pi i \cdot 2^3 = 16\pi i.$$

(c) Let $\mathcal{R} = \{z : \operatorname{Re} z < 4\}$, which is simply-connected. Then $f(z) = (z + 4)/(z - 4)$ is analytic on $\mathcal{R}$, and $\Gamma = \{z : |z - 1| = 2\}$ is a closed contour in $\mathcal{R}$. Hence, by Cauchy's Theorem,
$$\int_\Gamma \frac{z + 4}{z - 4} \, dz = 0.$$

(d) Let $\mathcal{R} = \mathbb{C}$, which is simply-connected. Then $f(z) = \sin z$ is analytic on $\mathcal{R}$, $\Gamma = \{z : |z - 1| = 2\}$ is a simple-closed contour in $\mathcal{R}$ and the point i lies inside Γ.

Hence, by Cauchy's Integral Formula,
$$\int_\Gamma \frac{\sin z}{z - i}\, dz = 2\pi i f(i)$$
$$= 2\pi i \sin i = -2\pi \sinh 1.$$

(e) First note that $z^2 - 4 = (z+2)(z-2)$ and that the point 2 lies inside $\Gamma = \{z : |z - 1| = 2\}$ and the point -2 lies outside Γ.

Let $\mathcal{R} = \{z : \operatorname{Re} z > -2\}$, which is simply-connected. Then $f(z) = z^2/(z+2)$ is analytic on $\mathcal{R}$, Γ is a simple-closed contour in $\mathcal{R}$ and the point 2 lies inside Γ. Hence, by Cauchy's Integral Formula,
$$\int_\Gamma \frac{z^2}{z^2 - 4}\, dz = \int_\Gamma \frac{z^2/(z+2)}{z - 2}\, dz$$
$$= 2\pi i f(2)$$
$$= 2\pi i \cdot \frac{4}{4} = 2\pi i.$$

2.2 The figure shows $\Gamma = \{z : |z - 1| = 3\}$ and the points relevant to parts (a), (b) and (c).

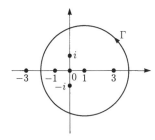

(a) Note that $z^2 - 1 = (z - 1)(z + 1)$ and that the points 1 and -1 lie inside Γ. So we find the partial fractions of $1/(z^2 - 1)$:
$$\frac{1}{z^2 - 1} = \frac{1/2}{z - 1} - \frac{1/2}{z + 1}.$$
Then
$$\int_\Gamma \frac{2z}{z^2 - 1}\, dz = \int_\Gamma \frac{z}{z - 1}\, dz - \int_\Gamma \frac{z}{z + 1}\, dz. \qquad (*)$$
Let $\mathcal{R} = \mathbb{C}$, which is simply-connected. Then $f(z) = z$ is analytic on $\mathcal{R}$, $\Gamma = \{z : |z - 1| = 3\}$ is a simple-closed contour in $\mathcal{R}$, and the points 1 and -1 lie inside Γ. Hence, by Cauchy's Integral Formula applied to the two integrals on the right-hand side of $(*)$,
$$\int_\Gamma \frac{2z}{z^2 - 1}\, dz = 2\pi i f(1) - 2\pi i f(-1)$$
$$= 2\pi i \cdot 1 - 2\pi i \cdot (-1) = 4\pi i.$$

(b) Note that $z^2 + 1 = (z - i)(z + i)$ and that the points i and $-i$ lie inside Γ. So we find the partial fractions of $1/(z^2 + 1)$:
$$\frac{1}{z^2 + 1} = \frac{i/2}{z + i} - \frac{i/2}{z - i} \qquad \text{(see page 15).}$$
Then
$$\int_\Gamma \frac{\sin 2z}{z^2 + 1}\, dz = \frac{i}{2} \int_\Gamma \frac{\sin 2z}{z + i}\, dz - \frac{i}{2} \int_\Gamma \frac{\sin 2z}{z - i}\, dz. \qquad (*)$$
Let $\mathcal{R} = \mathbb{C}$, which is simply-connected. Then $f(z) = \sin 2z$ is analytic on $\mathcal{R}$, $\Gamma = \{z : |z - 1| = 3\}$ is a simple-closed contour in $\mathcal{R}$, and the points $-i$ and i lie inside Γ. Hence, by Cauchy's Integral Formula applied to the two integrals on the right-hand side of $(*)$,
$$\int_\Gamma \frac{\sin 2z}{z^2 + 1}\, dz = \frac{i}{2} \cdot 2\pi i \cdot f(-i) - \frac{i}{2} \cdot 2\pi i \cdot f(i)$$
$$= -\pi \sin(-2i) + \pi \sin(2i) = 2\pi i \sinh 2.$$

(c) Note that $z(z^2 - 9) = z(z - 3)(z + 3)$, and that the points 0 and 3 lie inside Γ, but the point -3 lies outside Γ. So we find the partial fractions of $1/(z(z - 3))$:
$$\frac{1}{z(z - 3)} = \frac{1/3}{z - 3} - \frac{1/3}{z}.$$
Then
$$\int_\Gamma \frac{6 \cosh z}{z(z^2 - 9)}\, dz = 2 \int_\Gamma \frac{(\cosh z)/(z + 3)}{z - 3}\, dz$$
$$- 2 \int_\Gamma \frac{(\cosh z)/(z + 3)}{z}\, dz. \qquad (*)$$
Let $\mathcal{R} = \{z : \operatorname{Re} z > -\frac{5}{2}\}$, which is simply-connected. Then $f(z) = (\cosh z)/(z + 3)$ is analytic on $\mathcal{R}$, $\Gamma = \{z : |z - 1| = 3\}$ is a simple-closed contour in $\mathcal{R}$, and the points 0 and 3 lie inside Γ. Hence, by Cauchy's Integral Formula applied to the two integrals on the right-hand side of $(*)$,
$$\int_\Gamma \frac{6 \cosh z}{z(z^2 - 9)}\, dz = 2(2\pi i f(3)) - 2(2\pi i f(0))$$
$$= 4\pi i \frac{\cosh 3}{6} - 4\pi i \frac{\cosh 0}{3}$$
$$= \frac{2\pi}{3}(\cosh 3 - 2)i.$$

2.3 **(a)** Let $g = 1/f$. Then g is entire, since $|f(z)| \geq K > 0$ and f is entire.

Also g is bounded, since
$$|g(z)| = 1/|f(z)| \leq 1/K \quad (K \neq 0).$$
Hence, by Liouville's Theorem, g is a constant function and therefore f is a constant function.

(b) The function $f(z) = e^z$ is a counter-example. It is an entire function such that
$$|e^z| > 0, \qquad \text{for all } z \in \mathbb{C}.$$
But f is not a constant function.

Section 3

3.1 The figure shows $\Gamma = \{z : |z| = 2\}$ and points relevant to parts (a)–(e).

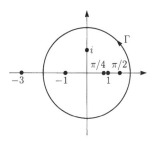

For parts (a), (b), (d) and (e), we take $\mathcal{R} = \mathbb{C}$, which is simply-connected.

(a) The function $f(z) = \cos z$ is analytic on $\mathcal{R}$, Γ is a simple-closed contour in $\mathcal{R}$ and the point $\pi/2$ lies inside Γ. Hence, by Cauchy's First Derivative Formula,
$$\int_\Gamma \frac{\cos z}{(z - \pi/2)^2}\, dz = 2\pi i f'(\pi/2)$$
$$= 2\pi i(-\sin(\pi/2)) = -2\pi i.$$

(b) The function $f(z) = \cosh \pi z$ is analytic on $\mathcal{R}$, Γ is a simple-closed contour in $\mathcal{R}$ and the point i is inside Γ. Hence, by Cauchy's Second Derivative Formula,

$$\int_\Gamma \frac{\cosh \pi z}{(z-i)^3} \, dz = \frac{2\pi i}{2!} f''(i)$$
$$= \pi i \cdot \pi^2 \cosh \pi i$$
$$= \pi^3 i \cos \pi = -\pi^3 i.$$

(c) Note that $z^2 + 2z - 3 = (z+3)(z-1)$ and that the point 1 lies inside Γ but the point -3 does not. Let $\mathcal{R} = \{z : \operatorname{Re} z > -\frac{5}{2}\}$. Then $f(z) = (\sin z)/(z+3)^2$ is analytic on $\mathcal{R}$, and Γ is a simple-closed contour in $\mathcal{R}$. Hence, by Cauchy's First Derivative Formula,

$$\int_\Gamma \frac{\sin z}{(z^2 + 2z - 3)^2} \, dz = \int_\Gamma \frac{(\sin z)/(z+3)^2}{(z-1)^2} \, dz$$
$$= 2\pi i f'(1)$$
$$= 2\pi i \cdot \frac{4\cos 1 - 2\sin 1}{4^3}$$
$$= \frac{1}{16}(2\cos 1 - \sin 1)\pi i.$$

$(f'(z) = ((z+3)^2 \cos z - 2(z+3)\sin z)/(z+3)^4)$

(d) The function $f(z) = \sin 2z$ is analytic on $\mathcal{R}$, Γ is a simple-closed contour in $\mathcal{R}$ and the point $\pi/4$ lies inside Γ. Hence, by Cauchy's nth Derivative Formula with $n = 4$,

$$\int_\Gamma \frac{\sin 2z}{(z - \pi/4)^5} \, dz = \frac{2\pi i}{4!} f^{(4)}(\pi/4)$$
$$= \frac{\pi i}{12} \cdot 2^4 \sin(2\pi/4)$$
$$= \tfrac{4}{3}\pi i.$$

(e) The function $f(z) = 1$ is analytic on $\mathcal{R}$, Γ is a simple-closed contour in $\mathcal{R}$ and the point -1 lies inside Γ. Hence, by Cauchy's nth Derivative Formula with $n = 10$,

$$\int_\Gamma \frac{1}{(z+1)^{11}} \, dz = \frac{2\pi i}{10!} f^{(10)}(-1)$$
$$= 0, \quad \text{since } f^{(10)}(-1) = 0.$$

3.2 Note that

$$z^4 - 2z^3 + z^2 = z^2(z^2 - 2z + 1)$$
$$= z^2(z-1)^2,$$

and that the points 0 and 1 lie inside $\Gamma = \{z : |z| = 3\}$. So we find the partial fractions for $1/(z^2(z-1)^2)$. Let

$$\frac{1}{z^2(z-1)^2} = \frac{A}{z} + \frac{B}{z^2} + \frac{C}{z-1} + \frac{D}{(z-1)^2}.$$

Multiplying both sides by $z^2(z-1)^2$, we obtain

$$1 = Az(z-1)^2 + B(z-1)^2 + Cz^2(z-1) + Dz^2.$$

Comparing the coefficients of z^3, z^2, z and constants, we obtain

$$\begin{aligned} z^3: & \quad 0 = A + C \\ z^2: & \quad 0 = -2A + B - C + D \\ z: & \quad 0 = A - 2B \\ 1: & \quad 1 = B. \end{aligned}$$

These simultaneous equations have solution

$$A = 2, \quad B = 1, \quad C = -2, \quad D = 1.$$

Hence

$$\frac{1}{z^4 - 2z^3 + z^2} = \frac{2}{z} + \frac{1}{z^2} - \frac{2}{z-1} + \frac{1}{(z-1)^2}.$$

Thus

$$\int_\Gamma \frac{e^{3z}}{z^4 - 2z^3 + z^2} \, dz$$
$$= 2\int_\Gamma \frac{e^{3z}}{z} \, dz + \int_\Gamma \frac{e^{3z}}{z^2} \, dz - 2\int_\Gamma \frac{e^{3z}}{z-1} \, dz$$
$$+ \int_\Gamma \frac{e^{3z}}{(z-1)^2} \, dz. \quad (*)$$

We now apply Cauchy's Integral Formula to the first and third integrals on the right-hand side of $(*)$ and Cauchy's First Derivative Formula to the other two. We take $\mathcal{R} = \mathbb{C}$, which is simply-connected. Then $f(z) = e^{3z}$ is analytic on $\mathcal{R}$, Γ is a simple-closed contour in $\mathcal{R}$ and the points 0 and 1 lie inside Γ.

We obtain

$$\int_\Gamma \frac{e^{3z}}{z^4 - 2z^3 + z^2} \, dz = 2(2\pi i f(0)) + 2\pi i f'(0)$$
$$- 2(2\pi i f(1)) + 2\pi i f'(1)$$
$$= 2(2\pi i e^0) + 2\pi i (3e^0)$$
$$- 2(2\pi i e^3) + 2\pi i (3e^3)$$
$$= 2\pi(2 + 3 - 2e^3 + 3e^3)i$$
$$= 2\pi(5 + e^3)i.$$

3.3 Assume that there exists an analytic function F such that $F'(z) = \operatorname{Re} z$, for $z \in \mathbb{C}$. Then, by the Analyticity of Derivatives, F' is analytic on $\mathbb{C}$. But $F'(z) = \operatorname{Re} z$, which is not analytic on $\mathbb{C}$. This contradiction implies that no such function F exists.

Section 4

4.1 In *these* solutions, we present only brief evaluations.

(a) By Cauchy's Theorem with $\mathcal{R} = \mathbb{C}$,

$$\int_{\Gamma_2} \sin z \, dz = 0.$$

(b) By Cauchy's Theorem with $\mathcal{R} = \mathbb{C}$,

$$\int_{\Gamma_2} \sin(z^2) \, dz = 0.$$

(c) By Cauchy's Theorem with $\mathcal{R} = \{z : \operatorname{Im} z > -\frac{1}{2}\}$,

$$\int_{\Gamma_2} \frac{1}{z+i} \, dz = 0.$$

(d) $\displaystyle\int_{\Gamma_1} z \sin z \, dz$ cannot be evaluated by the methods of this unit. Integration by parts and the Fundamental Theorem of Calculus are appropriate here.

(e) By Cauchy's First Derivative Formula with $\mathcal{R} = \mathbb{C}$,

$$\int_{\Gamma_3} \frac{\sin z}{z^2} \, dz = 2\pi i \sin'(0)$$
$$= 2\pi i \cos 0 = 2\pi i.$$

(f) By Cauchy's nth Derivative Formula with $n = 4$ and $\mathcal{R} = \mathbb{C}$,

$$\int_{\Gamma_3} \frac{\cosh z}{z^5} \, dz = \frac{2\pi i}{4!} \cosh^{(4)}(0)$$
$$= \frac{\pi i}{12} \cosh 0 = \frac{\pi i}{12}.$$

(g) By Cauchy's Theorem with $\mathcal{R} = \{z : -\pi < \operatorname{Im} z < \pi\}$,

$$\int_{\Gamma_3} \frac{z^5}{\cosh \frac{1}{2} z} \, dz = 0.$$

(h) By Cauchy's Integral Formula with $\mathcal{R} = \{z : \text{Im}\, z > -\frac{1}{4}\}$,

$$\int_{\Gamma_2} \frac{z}{4z^2 + 1}\, dz = \int_{\Gamma_2} \frac{z/(2z+i)}{2z - i}\, dz$$

$$= \frac{1}{2} \int_{\Gamma_2} \frac{z/(2z+i)}{z - \frac{1}{2}i}\, dz$$

$$= \frac{1}{2} \cdot 2\pi i \cdot (\tfrac{1}{2}i/(2 \cdot \tfrac{1}{2}i + i))$$

$$= \tfrac{1}{4}\pi i.$$

(i) $\displaystyle\int_{\Gamma_3} \text{Re}\, z\, dz$ cannot be evaluated by the methods of this unit. Parametrization is the appropriate method here.

4.2 Let $\mathcal{R} = \mathbb{C}$, which is simply-connected. Then $f(z) = \exp(z^n)$ is analytic on $\mathcal{R}$, $\Gamma = \{z : |z| = 1\}$ is a simple-closed contour in $\mathcal{R}$, and the point 0 lies inside Γ. Hence, by Cauchy's Integral Formula,

$$\int_{\Gamma} \frac{\exp(z^n)}{z}\, dz = 2\pi i f(0)$$

$$= 2\pi i \exp(0^n) = 2\pi i. \qquad (1)$$

Using the standard parametrization

$$\gamma(t) = e^{it} \qquad (t \in [0, 2\pi])$$

for Γ, we have

$$\int_{\Gamma} \frac{\exp(z^n)}{z}\, dz = \int_0^{2\pi} \frac{\exp(e^{int})}{e^{it}} \cdot ie^{it}\, dt$$

$$= i \int_0^{2\pi} \exp(\cos nt + i \sin nt)\, dt$$

$$= i \int_0^{2\pi} e^{\cos nt} e^{i \sin nt}\, dt$$

$$= i \int_0^{2\pi} e^{\cos nt}(\cos(\sin nt) + i \sin(\sin nt))\, dt$$

$$= -\int_0^{2\pi} e^{\cos nt} \sin(\sin nt)\, dt$$

$$+ i \int_0^{2\pi} e^{\cos nt} \cos(\sin nt)\, dt. \qquad (2)$$

Equating the imaginary parts in (1) and (2), we obtain

$$\int_0^{2\pi} e^{\cos nt} \cos(\sin nt)\, dt = 2\pi.$$